# THE GREEKS
## AND THEIR
# MYTHS

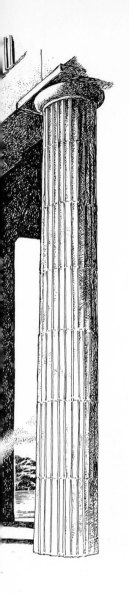

# THE GREEKS
## AND THEIR
# MYTHS

## The classic stories

retold by Michael Johnson

with an explanation of their origins and meanings

by John Sharwood Smith

*Illustrated by Peter Dennis*

Peter Lowe

THE AUTHORS
John Sharwood Smith was Reader in
Education and Head of Classics at
London University Institute of
Education from 1959–85. He was the
first Acting Secretary of the Joint
Association of Classical Teachers and
has published books on both classical
and educational topics.

Michael Johnson lectured at
universities in the United States
before becoming a full-time writer.
He has written books on literature,
history, the arts as well as biography
and original fiction. He has also
compiled anthologies, including folk
tales, children's literature, travel and
poetry.

THE ARTIST
Peter Dennis studied at Liverpool
College of Art and works as a full-
time artist. He has illustrated many
books, working in both full colour
and line and is a specialist in military
history.

Copyright © 1992 by Eurobook Limited

All rights reserved throughout the world.
No part of this publication may be reproduced,
stored in a retrieval system or transmitted,
in any form or by any means, electronic, mechanical,
photocopying, recording or otherwise, without the
prior written permission of Eurobook Limited.

British Library Cataloguing in Publication Data
Johnson, Michael 1937–
    The Greeks and their myths.
    1. Greek myths, ancient period
    I. Title   II. Sharwood Smith, John 1919—
292.13

ISBN 0-85654-656-9

# CONTENTS

# THE GREEKS

# THE MYTHS

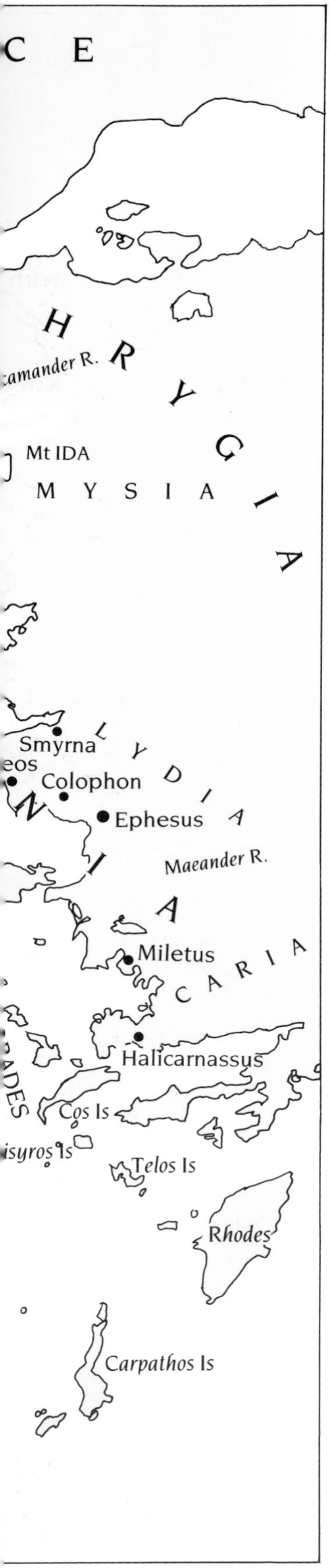

The map on the left shows place names including:

C E

Hamander R.

P H R Y G I A

Mt IDA

M Y S I A

Smyrna
eos
Colophon
L Y D I A
Ephesus

Maeander R.

Miletus
C A R I A

Halicarnassus

Cos Is

isyros Is
Telos Is

Rhodes

Carpathos Is

# INTRODUCTION

To us, myths from different cultures are either fascinating stories or subjects for anthropological investigation: we do not believe they are true. To the people who first told them this was far from being the case, for the stories we now classify as myths were both religious beliefs and an attempt to explain the phenomena of the natural world.

No one knows when people began to think about the world around them, to ask questions about their past and future, to speculate on the reasons for natural events, to wonder about life after death. For although scientists believe that humans evolved over two million years ago, and produce convincing reconstructions to show what they looked like, we can only guess at the thoughts and emotions of these early people.

Scanty evidence comes from archaeological excavations: more than 50,000 years ago a man was buried on a bed of flower petals: between 35,000 and 15,000 years ago elaborate burial customs developed and there were cave paintings and carved figures, probably of fertility goddesses.

Of course evidence of some kind of religious belief does not prove that myths in the form of stories were being told but since storytelling is universal amongst all societies from the most primitive to the most sophisticated, it is difficult not to draw that conclusion.

The earliest hard evidence of myths comes with the invention of writing, from the Sumerians between 3500 and 2030 BC and the Babylonians 2000 to 1100 BC. Egypt, whose first dynasty dates from 3000BC certainly had a comprehensive pantheon of gods and goddesses. On the other side of the world, Chinese myths are known from the eighth century BC.

The Greek myths are known first through the poets Homer and Hesiod. Hesiod's long poem 'The Theogeny' was concerned with the creation of the world and with the family of the gods. These poets composed their works some time in the eighth century BC, but there is no doubt that the Greek-speaking peoples had, like others, been developing their own beliefs over earlier centuries, absorbing influences from the civilizations with which they came into contact and passing on from generation to generation the stories of their gods.

# THE GREEKS

The Greeks who composed the versions of their myths which are to be found in this book lived between the seventh and the third centuries B C. There were Greeks living (and telling myths) long before then; just as there still are today. Indeed, many of the myths told here date back to a time hundreds, possibly many hundreds of years earlier than the seventh century B C and are still alive now in books, in films and on television. Some myths have been lost, and we only know that they existed because they are referred to in other writings. The most famous versions, however, and the ones that we have chosen, were written by Greek poets and playwrights between 700 and 100 B C.

The Greeks called themselves *Hellenes* and their country *Hellas* (and still do – 'Greeks' was the name the Romans gave them). They lived not only on the mainland and in the islands which are now labelled Greece but also in colonies all round the Mediterranean from southern Spain in the west to southern Turkey in the east.

The origins of Greek civilization, as far as we understand them, stretch back to the distant past, to the early Bronze Age around 3000 B C, even before Greek-speaking peoples had arrived in Greece. Fragments of its long history have been pieced together by archaeologists, linguists and historians, though much is still a matter of speculation. From about 700 B C, however, after the troubled times referred to by modern scholars as the Dark Ages of Greece, our knowledge of the Greeks begins to become much clearer. By then the Greeks had begun to develop the outlook on life and the institutions that make them of such great interest to us today. Experiments with democracy and the uninhibited discussion of political and moral ideas, speculation into the nature of the physical world, treatment of the human figure as a subject for art and an object to be perfected by athletic training – these are only some of the aspects of Greek civilization that arouse admiration and controversy today. The gods the Greeks worshipped and the heroes from their legendary past whose stories they told, were an important part of their lives; through the skill of their writers and artists, these myths and legends have survived to entertain and fascinate readers and listeners right up to the present day.

This bronze statue, dating from about 450 BC, was found on the seabed near Cape Artemisium, intact except for the eyeballs of coloured glass or stone and the weapon the figure was originally brandishing. The physique and features show that it represents one of the old Olympian gods: Zeus, Poseidon or Hades. The missing weapon would have made identification certain. Hades does not have a characteristic weapon. Poseidon's is the trident, which does not seem to fit in with the statue's stance. Zeus' thunderbolt, on the other hand, fits the attitude to perfection.

# THE MYTHS OF THE GREEKS

'The stories the Greeks tell are many and, in my opinion, ridiculous. What I write is what I believe to be true.'

This is one of the few fragments that have survived from the writings of Hecataeus of Miletus. He was himself a Greek, a traveller and writer who wrote on historical and geographical matters at the end of the sixth and beginning of the fifth century B C. As his contemptuous comment shows, he was among the first Greeks to believe that it was possible to give a better account of the world and its past than was to be found in the myths and legends which were accepted as wisdom by most educated Greeks of his day.

The attempts which he and other critically-minded Greeks made to give a reasoned description of the earth's surface and a reasoned account of past events laid the foundations of history and geography as they are studied today. *Historia* means 'enquiry' and *Geographia* means 'describing the Earth'. They are both Greek words. Fellow citizens of Hecataeus also began about this time an enquiry into the nature of the universe which led to modern philosophy on the one hand and, eventually, to modern science on the other.

One might easily suppose that once the Greeks could learn about the past through historical enquiry and about foreign lands through the writings of geographers they would no longer find any interest in their myths — the stories that Hecataeus thought ridiculous. Nothing could be further from the truth. The development of history, geography, philosophy and science as alternative ways of looking at the world and the past was an essential stage in the development of western civilization. Nevertheless the Greek myths went on being important to the Greeks

long after Hecataeus, and they are to this day the subject of much serious speculation by psychologists and anthropologists as well as by scholars who study religions.

## The nature of myths

What are myths and what are they for? These seem like two simple questions, but they turn out to be far from simple. Scholars who have studied myths have come up with some very different answers, not all of which can be easily proved wrong and none of which can be proved right.

For a start it is usually thought convenient to make a rough distinction between three kinds of myth: legends, folk tales and religious myths.

Legends are a sort of history. They touch on events which really happened, mention men and women who truly existed and take place in localities which can often be identified. Where it has been possible, as it has with some mediaeval legends, to check a legend against other evidence, it turns out that in the legends events have been wildly distorted, men and women often given totally different characters from their true characters and the localities where the events took place have been changed in a thoroughly misleading manner.

Folktales are full of trickery and magic, witches, giants, ogres, animals who can talk and other impossibilities. Like legends, they have their heroes and heroines. The heroes are very often cool and clever at tricking their way out of difficulties and danger, and the heroines are usually beautiful, kind and innocent; but both heroes and heroines are often quite different in character from the heroic and tragic warriors and queens of legend.

Religious myths (sometimes called 'pure' myths) are about matters of profound concern to human beings, such as: How did the world come into existence? Why do we have to die? Why do most of us have to work hard to keep alive? What is the nature of God, or the gods? How can

Mount Olympus, the home of the gods. Towering to a height of more than 2800m, the sheer peaks of the mountain are cold and inaccessible. The highest peak of all is known as the throne of Zeus. Recently the remains of a temple have been found on the mountain, linked by a sacred pathway to the city below.

To the Greeks, Mount Olympus was the highest mountain in the world but it was also a supernatural realm. There the immortals lived in sumptuous palaces, watching the activities of men and women below, savouring the sacrifices that were offered to them, feasting on ambrosia and drinking nectar from their golden goblets.

we please him—or her or them—so that we are protected and not punished? Other myths, not so obviously religious, are about matters of special concern to a particular tribe or people. They answer questions like: Why are our chiefs, or kings, always chosen in just such a way from this or that family? Why do our young men go through just such an initiation ceremony when they become adult? Why must marriages be performed just so and not in any other way? Often they are about the ownership of property by a particular family or clan or about friendly or hostile relations with a neighbouring tribe. The answer to all these questions is a story, a myth. Things are just so because a god, or a revered ancestor of the tribe, did such and such, and things have been just so ever since and must always remain so. In fact, before writing takes over from story-telling by word of mouth, things do not always have to remain so: the story is often subtly changed to fit new circumstances.

# How the myths came to us

For many thousands of years most people in the world did not know how to read and write. Ideas and information were communicated mainly by speech. Some things were communicated also by other means—by gesture (body language), images (carvings, paintings and the like) and enactment (dance and other ritual behaviour—what you did in a religious ceremony or when you came before the king or a high official), or by music. All these means of communication were used to hand on from generation to generation what were believed to be religious truths; but it was by word of mouth that myths, being stories, were most easily passed on.

Folktales have been collected by scholars over the last two centuries from all over the world. We know about Babylonian religious myths because archaeologists have dug up clay tablets on which the myths were written down by the priests whose duty it was to recite them. Greek

Theseus and the Minotaur, drawn on the inside of a sixth-century wine cup. Myths and legends have been used as propaganda many times in the course of history. In the late sixth and early fifth century, the Athenians promoted their legendary hero Theseus by depicting his exploits on the painted pottery which they were so successfully manufacturing and exporting all over the Greek world and beyond.

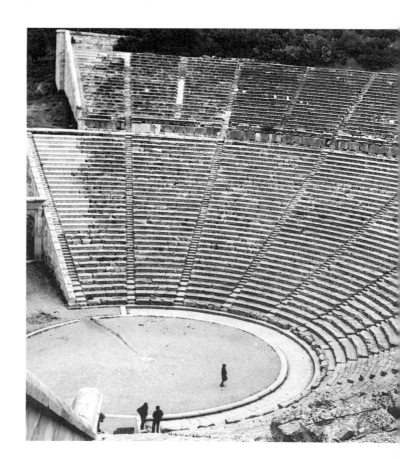

Epic poems were recited to large audiences by the rhapsodes (above), the successors of the bards who sang and played at Homeric feasts. Contests for both playwrights and rhapsodes were held at Epidaurus. Left: The theatre at Epidaurus, built in the fourth century BC, had seating for 14,000 people. Fifth-century audiences watched the performance of the great tragedies from backless wooden benches placed on a terraced semi-circle of earth. The actors were all men and wore masks, which enabled them each to take several parts and there was a chorus who sang and danced on a circular floor. The plays were given in daylight so there could be no lighting effects and scenery consisted only of the facade of a hut.

folktales and myths and legends have not come down to us from such an early stage in their development: we can guess that they were told and retold for hundreds of years but we only know them in the form they were given by the Greeks who used them as the subjects of their poems and plays. In turning the myths into literature the poets and playwrights combined many stories, some legends, some folktales, some religious myths, so any Greek myth that we come across is likely to include all three ingredients mixed up together.

In the course of time the Greeks were conquered by the Romans, who admired Greek civilization, learned Greek and read the Greeks' favourite poems and plays. Then, some Romans started to imitate the Greeks and wrote poems and plays in their own language, Latin. Most of these poems and plays were based on the Greek myths and legends. When the Roman Empire declined and came to an end and the countries which are now England, France, Spain and Italy were invaded and settled by barbarians, the Latin language survived as the language of the Christian church. The scriptures had all been translated from Hebrew and Greek into Latin, and the monks and bishops did all their reading and writing in Latin. They read the Bible and the lives of the saints, but for pleasure and relaxation they read the Latin versions of the old myths.

When English, French and German and the other European languages took over from Latin, among the first things that were written were new versions of the old stories. In English, Chaucer retold many of them. Shakespeare used them (*A Midsummer Night's Dream* is an example). French, Italian and German poets and playwrights used them and so did Keats and Shelley, and, when World War One began, many young men went off to fight on the Western Front with the idea that war would be as glorious as it appeared to be in the poems of Homer which they had learned at school.

And today the stories reappear in plays, films, television drama, and even in advertising.

# THE LAND OF GREECE

## Countrymen

Greece, though it is a beautiful land, is a hard land for a countryman to make a living from, and most Greeks were countrymen. Much of Greece is mountainous, heavily forested and snow-covered in winter. The lower slopes provide pasture in summer, but in winter the flocks, mostly goats and sheep, are brought down to the lowlands, to the edge of the cultivated land. The life of a shepherd in ancient times was lonely and hard and he had no friends among the farmers when his hungry goats strayed onto their land. Wheat grew sparsely on the thin soil and was usually planted between the trees in an olive grove. Olives were the one crop that flourished and olive-oil was used for cooking, for lighting (in oil lamps) and for cleaning oneself, much as we use soap. But war was common and the enemy could come and cut down the olive groves; in which case it was at least sixteen years before newly planted trees would bear a full crop of olives.

Grapes were the third of the three main crops of the Greek farmer, and vines and grapes can be attacked by disease. So life for the farmers was full of anxiety. If the population of a Greek state increased there was not enough food to feed

A shepherd's life in ancient Greece was a solitary one. Alone with the animals, it was easy to believe that the shifting patterns of light and shade were half glimpsed figures of the spirits of the woods and streams.

Poorer peasants did their own ploughing. For them the oxen were a very important investment and very cherished members of the household, sharing their masters' living quarters in wintertime. The picture shows a team of two oxen. They work so closely together that this is only obvious if you count the number of legs.

Pomegranates grew wild in ancient Greece and were also cultivated. In folktales, if you eat the food offered to you by supernatural beings you can never be free from them and in the myth of Persephone, a pomegranate seed was the cause of her remaining in the Underworld as the bride of Hades.

everyone, so those worst off had to be persuaded to take their chance in new lands across the sea. Even when the population was stable it only needed a bad harvest for the farmer and his family to face starvation, and even in a normal year his daughters would be undernourished for fear that there would not be enough food to keep the menfolk strong and healthy to work the farm, and to fight in the army whenever this was necessary.

Living so precariously, a Greek countryman wanted to make sure by prayer and sacrifice that he would have the gods on his side: not just the great gods of Mount Olympus—Zeus and Hera and Apollo and Artemis and the other eight Olympians—but the spirits of dead heroes and the goat-god Pan and the nymphs, who haunt the countryside and can do the farmer good or harm. These nymphs are the spirits of the woods, and especially of the streams and of the mountain springs—water was sacred and Greece in summer is a parched land. In the wilder parts of Greece many countrymen believed they had glimpsed nymphs or their male companions, the satyrs. If this happened a prudent countryman would look away for fear that he might be driven mad by an angry nymph or by the god Pan himself—the original creator of panic.

## Craftsmen

Even the craftsmen, such as the potters, metal-workers and stonemasons felt the need to pray and sacrifice to their patron, the god Hephaestus. Hephaestus had his forge in his dwelling on Mount Olympus where he made wonderful mechanical gadgets to amuse or to tease the other gods and goddesses. He was lame, like many blacksmiths (who needed muscular arms and shoulders for their job but had little need to use their legs). If Hephaestus was not honoured the pots of the potters might shatter in the kiln, the blacksmiths' iron turn brittle on the forge and the mason's stone splinter as he cut it from the quarry.

Harvesting olives, shown on a storage jar from the sixth century BC. Olives were a valuable crop, providing oil for cooking, lighting and washing. One hundred trees could yield 700 kilos of oil in a good year but the trees grow slowly and a farmer could lose his livelihood if they were destroyed by invading armies.

# Seafarers

Greeks who were not countrymen might have been sea-traders. The Mediterranean with its treacherous currents, rocky shores and sudden summer storms was perilous for Greek mariners who had no maps and no compasses and whose sails did not allow them to tack against the wind. They prayed and sacrificed to Zeus' brother Poseidon, Lord of the sea or to the sea nymphs, the Nereids, and their father Nereus, the wise old sea god, or to the wind gods, especially Boreas, the god of the North Wind which could suddenly blow up a storm, even in clear weather, and drive ships onto a rocky coast.

Above right: The inside of a shallow drinking vessel made by the great potter Ezekias in about 530 BC, shows Dionysus on board a typical warship with a projecting ram in the prow with which to stave in the sides of enemy vessels. The small platform is for marines to use when trying to board an enemy ship. The paddles at the rear are for steering: rudders had not been invented in ancient Greek times.

Crafts and trades
1. The shoemaker. A small boy has a sandal cut to the size and shape of his foot.
2. A fisherman, probably on his way to the agora (marketplace) in Athens where he or his wife might be a stallholder.
3. A helmet maker finishing a Corinthian helmet by smoothing the edges with a rasp.
4. A potter painting black glaze on to a bell-shaped bowl to be used for mixing wine and water.

# THE GREEK PAST

Myths and legends reflect—though very inaccurately—the past of the people who tell them. Often a Greek myth has several layers, each layer reflecting events that occurred—or beliefs that were adopted from other peoples—at one of the three main stages of the past history of Greece and of the eastern Mediterranean.

## The first stage: Minoan Crete

### (c.2000—c.1400 BC)

The earliest civilization that arose in the lands where the Greeks came to live was that which flourished in Crete between 2000 and 1400 BC. Thanks to excavations carried out at the beginning of this century, the Cretan civilization is less mysterious to us today than it was to the Greeks of the time of, say, Hecataeus. Nevertheless it is still full of puzzles. The historian Thucydides, who was born two generations later than Hecataeus, reckoned that the only trustworthy information contained in the legends about Crete was that there was a king of Crete called Minos who built up a navy, ruled the islands between Crete and Greece,

Minoan weapons and tools were made of bronze, and the Cretans' skill in working and decorating it became legendary. The bronze bowl below dates from the late Minoan period, the fifteenth century BC.

Bulls were particularly associated with Cretan civilization and clay models, probably used as votive offerings, are quite common. Vases in the shape of bulls are much rarer. This one is a rhyton, a type of vase used in religious ceremonies. Liquid would be poured into the animal's hollow body, then dripped out through its mouth as a libation to the gods.

planted colonies and made war on pirates. Thanks to the excavators, we now know that the rulers of Crete had at least five magnificent palaces and a lifestyle full of luxury and elegance. If we go to Crete we can look at the ruins of the palaces, at the bright, vivid pictures they had painted on their walls and the vases, jewellery and carved seal-stones which they used. At some time in the fifteenth century BC the largest of the Cretan palaces, Cnossus, came to be controlled by rulers from mainland Greece who spoke Greek (which the Cretans did not). Not very long afterwards Cnossus was sacked and burned. There were also severe earthquakes in Crete at this time and a powerful volcanic explosion on the little island of Thera, which deposited volcanic ash on Crete. From this time onwards this first stage of civilization in the eastern Mediterranean steadily declined. Whether the decline was due to destruction by sea raiders, to earthquakes, to the volcanic eruption or to a revolution on Crete, scholars have not so far been able to agree. They have named the civilization 'Minoan' from the legendary King Minos.

Above: The Throne Room of the Palace of Minos at Cnossus, as it was restored in 1930. When Sir Arthur Evans began to excavate the room in 1900 he found walls with the remains of frescoes and traces of original plaster. There were also signs of charred wooden columns, evidence of the fire that destroyed the palace in the fifteenth century BC. The throne itself was set on a raised platform and had originally been covered with painted plaster.

## The second stage: Mycenaean Greece (c.1400 – c.1150 BC)

During the time that the Cretans were ruling the sea Greek-speaking people had moved into Greece from the north — no one knows precisely where from — and settled, mainly in central and southern Greece. This had been happening since some time before 1700 BC. From about 1400 BC their rulers built themselves palaces on strong, carefully chosen sites, usually on rocks or hillsides. They employed mass labour and fortified their palaces with masonry so massive that later Greeks thought they must have recruited giants from abroad to build the walls. The rulers were warlike, frequently fighting one another, and they were wealthy, acquiring their wealth by trading with cities in Egypt, Syria,

Palestine and Cyprus. With this wealth they employed highly skilled craftsmen to make such things as gold-inlaid bronze daggers, gold cups, jewels and lifelike gold death-masks. The death-masks, weapons and other precious objects have survived to this day because they were buried with the rulers in their magnificent tombs.

The most impressive palace and the most impressive tombs were in southern Greece at a site named Mycenae. Scholars have named this second stage of Greek history The Mycenaean Age after this site.

The best remembered event of the Mycenaean Age was the Trojan War. Troy, according to the legends, was a great and rich city on the Asian side of the narrow sea that divides Europe from Asia. A Trojan prince, so the stories told, came to Greece and carried off the beautiful wife of the king of Sparta. This king's brother, Agamemnon, the King of Mycenae, led a great expedition to Troy, to sack the city and bring her back. The expedition was successful, but only after a ten year siege. Many of the Mycenaean princes, however, met with disasters during the war or after their return home.

The next generation—the sons and daughters— were embroiled in bitter family feuds. With their

Tiryns was built on a small outcrop of rock on the plain of Argos, only about ten miles from Mycenae and scholars are puzzled that two powerful fortresses could have coexisted so close to one another. The earliest walls were built of small symmetrical stones, later extensions were made of huge irregular blocks (right). The impression made by Tiryns today is of a grim and gloomy fortress, but archaeologists have found there gold rings, painted vases, and fragments of frescoes.

Left: The circle of graves within the fortress walls at Mycenae. Shaft graves, dated to the sixteenth and fifteenth centuries BC were simple pit shafts lined with stone. By the twelfth century BC, when Agamemnon ruled in Mycenae, kings were buried in massive stone burial-chambers of a kind nicknamed 'beehive' because of their shape. Some were over 14m in diameter and 13m in height, with an entrance surmounted by a lintel weighing about 100 tons.

Above: The Lion Gate at Mycenae. Mycenae was built on a rocky hillside which dominated the fertile plain stretching south-eastwards to the gulf of Argos. There was a small fortified palace on the site from the sixteenth century BC. In the thirteenth century BC the area of the acropolis was doubled and this imposing fortified entrance was built. It is placed so that an attacker would be exposed to the defenders' slings and arrows on both flanks.

Above: This mask, made of gold and silver alloy, was found in a 'shaft' grave. Other graves contained swords with handles of precious metals, decorated vessels, a gold cup, engraved gold disks and delicately made personal ornaments of many kinds.

When the pioneer excavator Heinrich Schliemann found this mask he assumed that he had looked upon the face of Agamemnon. More scientific dating methods proved that it had been buried three or four centuries before Agamemnon's time.

Above: Ezekias, the great fifth-century vase painter, has here painted Achilles and Ajax taking time off from the Trojan war to play a board game. Ajax is saying, three (tria) and Achilles, who was always better than anyone else at anything, is saying four (tessara).

Left: Scenes of a warrior putting on his armour were a favourite subject of epic poets and also of vase painters.
'Patroclus clad himself in shining bronze. First he put round his shins a fine pair of greaves fitted with silver anklets. Then he fixed on his chest the breastplate of swift-footed Achilles adorned with stars. Around his shoulders he slung the bronze, silver-studded sword and then the mighty shield. On his sturdy head he set the well made helmet above which a horsehair crest nodded fiercely. He also took two strong spears which fitted snugly into the palm of his hand.' *Iliad* 16, 130-139.

Right: Fifth-century BC spear and helmet, from the grave of Dendas, a Hoplite soldier buried with his bronze armour in Sicily. Corinthian helmets were worn by Greek infantrymen from the seventh century BC onwards. When not in battle, the warrior wore his helmet on the back of his head, like Achilles (above).

grandchildren the stories come to an end.

How much of what is told in the stories is fact and how much fiction is something which scholars have argued about for centuries. In the last hundred and twenty years archaeology has provided much evidence, but the evidence is of the sort that can be interpreted in many ways. What at the moment seems to be certain is that there was a powerfully fortified, though quite small, city on the Asian side of the Hellespont. This city was destroyed, not for the first time, in the thirteenth century B C. It also seems certain that the Mycenaean civilization of Greece came to a fairly abrupt end during the twelfth century B C. The palace fortresses were destroyed and their sites abandoned. At the same time some new sites were occupied by Mycenaeans on the eastern side of the Aegean Sea, in Cyprus and on the south coast of what is now Turkey

# The third stage: the Greek Dark Ages (c.1100 – c.700 B C)

The name 'Dark Ages' has been given to the three or four centuries that followed the collapse of the Mycenaean civilization. They are 'dark' in the same way that the centuries are 'dark' that followed the final destruction by barbarian tribes of the western Roman Empire in the fifth century AD. There was a great deal of violence and destruction of property, leaving very little of the kind of evidence that would enable a historian to construct a clear picture of what actually happened.

In this respect the Greek Dark Ages are much darker to us than are the western European Dark Ages. In Europe, the practice of writing chronicles was well established in the Christian monasteries and survived the times of violence. By contrast, in the Mycenaean Age the only kind of writing was that used to record the details of slaves, sheep and materials in the fortress palaces; it was known only to specially trained clerks and quickly forgotten when the palaces were destroyed. So there is very little to tell us what was going on in the Greek world for some 400 years, except what can be dug out of the ground. Something can also be learned about the movements of the Greek-speaking population of Greece and the eastern Aegean from studying the different dialects of Greek as far as these can be reconstructed. There is one other source of information—the myths and legends. Myths and legends, however, as we have already said, are a very unreliable guide to historical truth.

## The migrations

Throughout the Dark Ages the memory of the Mycenaean warriors, their raids and sieges, their palace plots and romances, their sea adventures and foreign encounters was kept alive by the bards—the singers who entertained the warrior chieftains and their followers when they could relax from the struggle for survival. Many of the chieftains of communities in southern and central Greece fled, it seems, as refugees, to Attica (the country of Athens). They helped the Athenians to repel bands seeking to invade Attica before setting out, presumably with small groups of followers, across the sea to the western coasts of what is now Turkey. There they found coastal sites with good harbours, preferably on a peninsula with only a narrow neck of land to defend against an attack from the mainland. With this site as a base they made friends with the natives or else attacked them, killing their men and making slaves (or wives) of their women and children. And there they settled, living, precariously at first, from farming and fishing, trading and piracy. They built a wall round their settlement and if the settlement prospered, it grew too big for its first walls and new walls would have to be built, together with a temple for the image of their patron god, or goddess to live in, and a market-place surrounded by porticos. Eventually the settlers would build a theatre and a wrestling-school for athletic training and their settlement would

The Acropolis at Athens. Here, in Mycenaean times, stood the palaces of the kings. It was a fortified outcrop of rock, like the site of Mycenae. Unlike Mycenae, Athens survived the Dark Ages intact and the Acropolis became the site of the city's most important temples. These were destroyed by the Persians in 480 BC. After some 40 years they were rebuilt and the Parthenon, the Temple of Athene, became for its architecture and sculpture the most admired monument in the ancient world.

become a typical Greek city state, like the city states that were beginning to develop on the mainland.

The city states were often at war with one another, trying to enlarge their territory at one another's expense. Some of them were ruled by kings, but the kings were expected to listen to the advice of the leading aristocrats. In other city states the aristocrats had already deposed their kings and ruled by themselves.

In some of the city states the people who had been living in the area before the Dark Ages had become serfs, semi-slaves who were obliged to till the soil for the benefit of other Greeks who had arrived during the Dark Ages as conquerors. Full slavery, however, was more common than

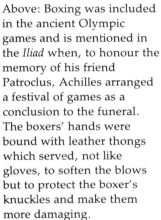

Above: Boxing was included in the ancient Olympic games and is mentioned in the *Iliad* when, to honour the memory of his friend Patroclus, Achilles arranged a festival of games as a conclusion to the funeral. The boxers' hands were bound with leather thongs which served, not like gloves, to soften the blows but to protect the boxer's knuckles and make them more damaging.

serfdom in ancient Greece. Prisoners of war, women and children captured in the storming of a city or kidnapped by pirates, and sometimes citizens who could not pay their debts, were made slaves—the property of their masters who might treat them kindly but could exploit them, punish them or sell them to other masters as and when they wished.

# The rise of classical Greece
## (c.600—c.300 B C)

By 600 B C there were no longer any kings except in a very few city states. Instead many city states were ruled by dictators (the Greeks call them 'tyrants' whether they were good, as several were, or bad) who championed the poorer people against the aristocrats. The cavalry warfare in which the aristocrats had excelled had given way to infantry warfare in which citizens who could afford the arms and armour of the heavily armed infantrymen had become the backbone of the city states' armies. Though warfare was always breaking out between city states this was also a time when poetry and music flourished, trade too, and also athletics (the Olympic Games were first held at Olympia in 776 B C).

During the sixth century a sophisticated civilization developed in the city states which had been founded as colonies on the coastline of Asia Minor (modern Turkey) and on the islands nearby. All these city states—but especially the city state of Miletus—had been stimulated by contacts with older and wealthier civilizations further east. Through these they had learned about the ideas and discoveries of the very ancient civilizations of Babylonia and Syria. Since 600 B C there had been in these Greek colonies men who criticized traditional ideas about the earth, the heavens and the gods and put forward creative ideas of their own.

Until the mid-sixth century B C the Greeks of Asia Minor had been very well placed for developing their civilization without interference, but in the second half of the century an aggressive new empire arose to the east of them, in the lands of ancient civilization. This was the powerful empire of the Persians, which expanded rapidly towards the Aegean Sea. The Greeks of Asia Minor were conquered (Miletus was destroyed) and they lost, firstly, their political freedom and, eventually, their prosperity and their intellectual vigour. From the beginning of the fifth century B C onwards the intellectual leadership of Greek civilization passed to the city states of the mainland, in particular to Athens, where it remained until the conquests of Alexander in 334-323 B C led to the formation of new intellectual centres at Alexandria, Rhodes and Pergamum.

# CHRONICLERS OF THE MYCENAEAN AGE

During the centuries of hardship and violence that followed the Mycenaean Age, the deeds of the Mycenaean warriors of Greece came to seem greater and more glorious than any deeds that would ever be performed again, and the warrior heroes themselves came to be thought stronger, braver, swifter, more skilful at fighting than any warriors who came after them. When the colonists had developed their own civilization and style of life these idealized Mycenaean heroes acquired also virtues of a gentler, more civilized and sophisticated kind. They were portrayed as capable of tact, courtesy, generosity to an enemy, respect for women and family affection—not that they were shown as always behaving at this high standard, but their lapses into violence, boastfulness, and discourtesy were treated as lapses, not as evidence of masterful virility. This, however, may be largely due to the genius of one man (or two, as some scholars think)—the bard (or bards) known to later Greeks by the name of Homer.

Homer, composing not long after the Dark Ages were over, some time between 850 and 750 B C, took two themes from the stories which bards had been retelling in song from generation to generation, ever since the Mycenaean Age. Homer's two themes are very different: the one a series of tragic episodes of the Trojan war, centred round the invincible hero Achilles and the courageous but less powerful Trojan leader Hector; the other a theme of sea travel, adventure, resourceful escapes and a homecoming to a palace infested with enemies who had to be exterminated by cool resource and determination. These two poems, the *Iliad* and the *Odyssey*, became in some respects like a bible for all Greeks from the time they were composed, and for a thousand years after. When a new way of writing, much simpler than the Mycenaean, was invented, Homer's poems were collected by Peisistratus, the man who had made himself dictator (tyrant) of Athens in the middle of the sixth century B C. He had them written down so that they could never again be sung or recited in a different way.

Education was at first something for aristocrats only and consisted in learning athletics and music and poetry, and the poetry they learned was first and foremost the *Iliad* and the *Odyssey*. Later, middle-class children received education too, and they also learned athletics, music and poetry—first and foremost the *Iliad* and the *Odyssey*.

The vase painters were more concerned with artistic effect than with realism. Hoplite armour such as these warriors are wearing does not make much sense in single combat. It was developed for battles fought in serried ranks where each person's right flank was protected by the shield of the man on his right.
Greek vase painters showed warriors wearing the armour of their own times, even when the men were heroes of the Mycenaean Age.

## The Heroic Age

Though Homer was far and away the greatest of the bards in the judgement of the Greeks, there were other poems about the battles and other events of the Mycenaean Age — 'epics', the Greeks called them. These are now lost but we know something of their stories because they were frequently referred to by Greek playwrights and poets, and were later collected by Greek antiquarians who picked them out of the works of the poets and put them together into dictionaries of mythology. From the poet Hesiod (who composed poems about the birth of the gods and the races of men who had inhabited the world in far off times) the Greeks learned to call the Mycenaean Age the Age of Heroes. The poets explained its end and the destruction of the Mycenaean palaces by telling that the descendants of the hero-god Heracles returned to southern Greece at the head of a Greek tribe called the Dorians, to reclaim their ancestral kingdom. When the Dark Ages were over, people speaking a Dorian dialect of Greek were in occupation of most of southern Greece, so it looks as if there is some truth in this story.

After the Dark Ages, Greek aristocrats liked to believe that they were descended from one of the heroes of the Age of Heroes. Since most of the heroes were conceived as the result of the rape or seduction of a mortal woman by a god, this had the flattering result of making them descendants of gods.

## Hecataeus again

Since the widespread adoption of the new way of writing, schools had come into existence. In consequence, storytelling was no longer the only way of communicating wisdom. Even before the time of Hecataeus there had been citizens of Miletus who had written books giving theories of how the world had come into existence — theories very different from the myths of Homer and Hesiod. From the nearby city of Colophon came a Greek who criticized Homer for describing the gods as if they were in the habit of committing all the crimes and follies that men were guilty of. It was absurd, he said, for Homer to suppose that the gods were just like men. No doubt, he said, if horses or oxen could paint, the gods they painted would look like horses and oxen. Homer, however, was so revered that criticizing his stories about the gods made very little impression. The Greeks continued to pray and sacrifice to them and the poets continued to retell the myths about them in poems and plays. Of the plays that have survived only those of Euripides raise difficult questions about the immoral behaviour of the Olympian gods, and we know that such questions were not agreeable to everyone in his audience.

# THE VALUE OF MYTHS

All through the ages there have been scholars who have tried to account for the existence and influence of myths. This has been especially so in the last hundred and fifty years. One of the wisest suggestions made is that human beings must have beliefs that enable them to make sense of the world they live in. Terrible experiences can be endured and men and women can adapt their way of life to survive catastrophes. What, however, human beings cannot endure is chaos—that is to say the experience of finding that none of the things that are happening to them makes any sense at all.

The Greek countryman lived his precarious existence with no experts from the Ministry of Agriculture to tell him why his crops were blighted, or his flocks sick, no medical expert to explain why his only son had suddenly become feverish and died, and no weathermen to explain why an unseasonable hailstorm had damaged his vines. Instead he knew from myths and folktales that humans had always been afflicted with suffering and misfortune ever since the first woman in her inquisitiveness had let all the evils out of the jar given her by the gods. He knew that in the countryside there were many powerful spirits he could have offended. He knew that the God Apollo and his sister Artemis could bring sudden sickness and death. Almost all the experiences he or any other Greek could encounter would be in harmony with the stories he knew about the world and its past.

We do know of one occasion when chaos seemed to have come to a Greek city. Athens at the height of her prosperity had embarked on the calculated risk of a war with Sparta, the most powerful state in Greece. All calculations were upset when a devastating plague broke out in Athens. Athens was crowded with many refugees from the countryside, and men, women and children died in agony in their hundreds.

Before the plague ceased about one third of the population had perished. It was impossible during the plague to bury the dead with the proper ceremonies since people were dying too fast. Often whole households succumbed, leaving no one to attend to their needs as they lay dying or to bury them when they were dead. The temples were full of the corpses of people who had gone there to implore help from the gods. Corpses were even thrown without ceremony onto funeral pyres prepared for others. Yet burial of near relatives was a sacred duty for Greeks and disrespect for the dead outraged their religious beliefs. These beliefs were expressed in the traditional funeral rites, and myths told of the disgrace and spiritual pollution incurred by those who neglected their duty of giving a proper burial to the dead. It was even more disturbing to the Athenians' religious beliefs when it became obvious that the plague attacked good people just as much as, if not more than, bad people. Unselfish citizens who nursed stricken relatives or friends were, if anything, more likely to catch the plague than the selfish who thought only of their own safety. Neither did those who had always been most conscientious in observing the ceremonies of

Above: This public inscription from fifth-century BC Crete sets out laws to deal with marriage, divorce, property disputes and other such matters. The late seventh and early sixth centuries BC were a time of great lawgivers who were entrusted with the task of settling violent conflicts between the aristocrats and the poor. Thanks to writing and literacy the laws they made became public property and justice could no longer be so easily corrupted.

Below: A young man is about to leave for the war. He has his shield on his left arm and grips the spear in his left hand. He has not yet put on his breastplate, greaves and helmet and he has put down his sword to make an offering at the household altar for his safe return. His young wife is pouring some wine from a wine flask into a shallow bowl for him to pour a few drops on to the altar.

prayer and sacrifice fare any better than those who had been lax. Did the gods then, the Athenians wondered, no longer care what men did or did not do?

This terrible experience and its consequences were described in detail by the historian Thucydides. He himself caught the plague (but recovered) and observed its effects on others. Their sufferings, he wrote, were greater than a human being could be expected to bear. The moral effects were as startling as the physical progress of the plague. Gross self-indulgence in the pleasures of the moment became the normal pattern of behaviour and no one was restrained from any wickedness by a sense of honour, by the prospect of punishment or by fear of the gods.

We in our civilization are, by contrast with the Greeks, provided with scientific theories of cause and effect for just about anything that can happen to us. Though in fact only a few experts properly understand the theories, yet the rest of us listen more or less intelligently to the experts' explanations and feel that our experiences, good and bad, are in harmony with all the other beliefs we hold about the universe. Science, however, tells only how things happen, not—in any fundamental sense—why. If we suffer some unbearable misfortune, we may find ourselves asking in desperation, 'Why did this have to happen to *me*?' or 'What have *I* done to deserve this?' To such questions science has no satisfying answer. Likewise when a whole community—a nation or ethnic group—has suffered humiliation and cruelty at the hands of others—ruthless occupation of their country, for instance, concentration camps, pogroms or genocide—the comfortable idea that scientific progress is steadily making the world a better, happier place to live in must seem like a very bad joke.

On such occasions science has no answers and more comfort may be found in myths that embody the wisdom and experience of many generations of men and women who have lived and suffered on our earth.

Left: Youth at a tomb (450—425 BC). The outline of the young man's body shows through where paint has worn away from the vase surface. This type of vase, known as a *lekythos*, was used for containing olive oil. Well preserved examples have often been found in graves and they were frequently used for making offerings of oil to the dead.

Below: Animal sacrifices were usually important state occasions. Oxen were carefully groomed and their horns gilded. They must appear to go to their sacrifice willingly, so the sacrificial knife was hidden at the bottom of a sacred basket and covered with barley grain. At the place of sacrifice the basket was carried round and the congregation threw the grain at the oxen. Then the priest (or priestess) cut a few hairs from the oxen's foreheads and the attendants raised each animal's head towards the sky (if the sacrifice was to an Olympian god) and cut its throat.

# THE MYTHS
## IN THE BEGINNING

Before us were our fathers, and before them were those who once lived in the land, men and women who were not of our people. We try to understand the order of the world and we listen to voices that have come from far away in our past. But we are uncertain of many things and our understanding does not go beyond the first emptiness, the void of Chaos.

The poets have taught us much. They have looked as best they can, with dim human eyes, into the generations of the gods, but about the first things we can say only this: in the beginning Chaos came into being.

Chaos brought forth Ge, the wide Earth, which is the home of the immortal gods, and Ge had with her Tartarus, a dark place sunk in the depths below the ground. Then Eros arose, the immortal who sends passion to loosen the limbs and govern the hearts of men and gods. From Chaos also came Darkness and Night, called Erebus and Nyx. And these two, seeing that there was as yet no light upon the world, lay together and brought forth Aether, the luminous air, and Hemera, the day.

Then Ge by herself gave birth to Uranus, the Heavenly Sky, a being equal to her in greatness and power. He covered her entirely, and so made firm and steadfast the everlasting dwelling-place of the gods.

Some tell another tale, maintaining that all earthly and heavenly things came from the stream of Oceanus, the river that runs round the world, and that his wife Tethys was the mother of all. Whether this goddess is called Ge or Tethys, all acknowledge her and invoke her as the Great Mother. From the time when our memory began, the poets have praised her: 'Earth is mother of all, the foundation of everything that is, the eldest of beings who supports all creatures and all things. All hail to the holy and boundless Goddess, Mother of Gods, and bride to the star-studded heavens.'

## The Titans, children of Earth and Sky

When Uranus, the Heavenly Sky, was formed, Mother Earth mated with him and brought forth the first race of divine children, those who are known as the Titans. These were Coeus and Crius, Oceanus, Hyperion and Iapetus. With them came the goddesses Theia and Rhea, Themis and Mnemosyne, Phoebe and Tethys. Last of all, Cronus was born, a sly and fearsome child who hated his father.

Ge laboured again and gave birth to the powerful Cyclopes and to three fearsome giants, each of whom had fifty heads and a hundred hands. No-one is certain about the nature of these beings but they know that the three Cyclopes later became smiths to the gods, making thunderbolts and lightning as well as ornaments and armour of bronze and iron. They were called Cyclopes, or 'Round Eyes', because each had a single eye in the middle of his forehead. But others say these people were just a race of savage giants who lived in Sicily, brutal and ignorant monsters with plenty of brawn and little brain.

These sons of Earth and Heaven were strong and unruly and terrible to look at, and their father Uranus hated them from the beginning. As each struggled to be born Uranus hid the monstrous infant in the huge, comforting body of Ge, the Earth, and it pleased him to prevent his children from coming into the light. But Ge groaned under her burden, straining to be delivered of her children until, unable to bear it any longer, she planned a way to be released.

She forged an iron sickle and called her elder children together. 'Now, my sons,' she said, 'who will listen to me and avenge the evil done by your father? For he has done shameful things.' But they were afraid and did not answer.

At last, Cronus came forward. 'Mother,' he said, 'I will do it, for I despise our father, who shames us with his deeds.'

### Where did the gods come from?

'It was Hesiod and Homer who first taught the Greeks all about the gods, gave them their names, described them and explained how they should be honoured and what were the special arts and skills they should be worshipped for.'

So wrote the historian Herodotus who lived from about 485 to about 425 B C.

We talk of the ancient Greeks, naturally, since their civilization flourished long before ours. The ancient Greeks themselves, however, considered that they were anything but ancient. This was because they compared themselves to the Egyptians whose civilization was already two thousand years old when Homer and Hesiod wrote about the gods in the eighth century B C.

Greeks who travelled to Egypt told stories, some of them probably true, about Egyptian priests who pointed to their monuments and inscriptions to prove the great age of their civilization. 'You Greeks are all children,' a priest says in one of these stories, 'because you have no ancient traditions and no ancient learning.'

Hecataeus, a Greek aristocrat who lived about sixty years before Herodotus, claimed to know his family tree for fifteen generations, his sixteenth ancestor being a god. 'Nonsense,' said the Egyptian priests. They could trace their ancestors for three hundred and forty-five generations and none of these had been a god. So there could not have been any gods on earth at the time of Hecataeus' sixteenth ancestor, nor for long before that.

Herodotus thought that the Greek gods had come, via the poems of Homer and Hesiod, from Egypt. Scholars now think that Hesiod's stories of the creation of our world came mostly from the ancient civilizations of Babylonia. The Babylonian stories became known to other civilizations of the Near East and were regularly reshaped and retold many times. One of the stories that resembles Hesiod's account of the creation of heaven and earth is a hymn that was recited each new year in Babylon, glorifying the god Marduk and telling how he separated the sky from the earth. Clay tablets show that

Then Ge gave Cronus the sickle and hid him in an ambush. That night, when love-sick Uranus came to cover the Earth, Cronus reached out his left hand, took hold of Uranus, and with the sickle cut off his father's genitals. He flung the severed parts towards the sea. Then drops of blood, falling on the ground, fertilized once more the womb of Earth which brought forth the giants, the nymphs called the Meliai, and the avenging Furies known as the Erinyes. The severed flesh of the god fell into the sea, and from the foam that frothed around it sprang the goddess Aphrodite. Rising out of the sea, she made her way to the island of Cythera, a place forever after famous for her worship. There she was joined by Eros and Desire, and the three immortals, putting their influence together, cast irresistible spells to agitate the hearts of men and gods.

When Cronus had done his brutal work, his father Uranus no longer approached Ge in the night. Heaven and Earth retreated apart, and the first generation of the gods was complete.

this was known in Syria, so Greeks who had begun to trade there after the Dark Ages ended in about 700 B C, could have brought it from Syria to Greece not long before the time of Hesiod; or else it could have been heard by Mycenaean traders centuries earlier and then told and retold throughout the Dark Ages. If you asked Hesiod where he got his stories, he would tell you (as he does at the beginning of his long poem) that he learned them from the Muses, daughters of Zeus and goddesses of song and all other forms of culture. They came to him when he was a shepherd looking after his lambs on Mount Helicon. They inspired him with poetry and told him to sing of the everlasting gods.

Those who want their stories to be rational, not mysterious, will not be satisfied with that account, but most Greeks were quite satisfied to believe, as many people do today, that poets were inspired. For the Greeks that inspiration came from the god Apollo or from the nine Muses and the poets' explanation of the origin of the world was therefore perfectly acceptable.

# The reign of Cronus

The young usurp the place of the old. The task of Uranus was over, the rule of Cronus began.

Some say that this was the Golden Age of the world, when life was innocent and happy, and the earth produced every kind of good thing without effort. But the ancient poets, whom we most respect, had another tale to tell.

The six female and six male deities who were the first children of Earth and Heaven, came together as husband and wife. Phoebe joined with Coeus, Theia with Hyperion, Tethys with Oceanus, Themis with Iapetus, Mnemosyne with Crius and Rhea with the victorious Cronus.

Cronus now reigned among the gods but reigned uneasily. When he had first taken Uranus' place, he had at once released his captive brothers, the Cyclopes and the hundred-handed giants, from their dark place within the earth. Later, suspicious of any rival to his power, he sentenced them once more to the dark depths of Tartarus. He who had treated Uranus so brutally had reason also to fear his own children: both Earth and Heaven had warned him that he, too, was destined to be overthrown. Cronus was afraid. As his wife Rhea gave birth to each of his children, he snatched up the baby and swallowed it. In this way he devoured Hestia, Demeter and Hera, Hades and Poseidon. Cronus, the jealous god, sat baleful through the night, keeping watch on Rhea, ready to swallow each child.

For Rhea, the mother, this was an agony and she petitioned her own parents, Ge and Uranus, to help her. Taking pity on her, they told her the secret fate of her family and took her destiny in hand. When Rhea was big with her youngest son, Zeus, Ge came in darkness and carried her off to Lyktos, in Crete. There the baby was born safely and Mother Earth took the child and hid it in a cave on the sheltered slopes of Mount Aegaeon. Then she chose a large stone, wrapped it in the baby's swaddling clothes and gave it to Cronus, who wasted no time in stuffing it into his belly.

## The Golden Age

Stories about gods and men came to the Greeks from many different sources. We should not, therefore, be surprised to find Greek myths which contradict one another. Nor is it so surprising that Hesiod can, in one of his poems, make Cronus a brutal and jealous tyrant and, in another, say that he presided over a happy Golden Age when there was no disease, no old age and no necessity for anyone to work.

There are two ways of looking at the past—even today. It can be thought of as a cruel and turbulent time, when men lived by the law of the jungle. Alternatively the past can be seen as a time when life was simple and carefree and there was no wealth or luxury to tempt men and women to greed, avarice and crime. Many civilizations have imagined a Golden Age in the remote past when men and animals lived together in peace and harmony and there was no toil, sickness or old age. Hesiod, as a farmer, was very aware that in the Greece of his time ill-health was common, a poverty-stricken old age was hard to bear and only hard work could keep a family from starvation. So for him a story which told that life had once been all leisure and happiness was too interesting to leave out of his account of the world and its past, even though it did not fit in with what he had already said about the rule of Cronus.

# The battle of the gods

As the seasons passed and Zeus grew to his full power in Crete, the cunning of Ge and her daughter Rhea at last induced Cronus to vomit up the children he had swallowed. First, he spewed out the stone which he had taken for his youngest son, and Zeus placed that stone in Pytho, in the valley of Parnassus, as a sign and a remembrance to later men.

Then Cronus vomited forth the rest of his children. At the same time Zeus also released once more the giant brothers of Cronus. There emerged into the light not only the hundred-handed giants but also the Cyclopes who, in gratitude, armed Zeus with the weapons of thunder and lightning. At this time, too, they gave to Hades a helmet of invisibility and to Poseidon a powerful, three-pronged trident, forged and tempered in the caverns of their rocky prison under the earth.

The rivalry between the generations of the immortals now erupted into full battle. The new gods who were the children of Cronus challenged the old Titans who were the children of Uranus. For ten years the struggle continued. The Titans held their stronghold on Mount Othrys and the younger gods sallied out bitterly from Mount Olympus. The battles were long and fierce and undecided, until Zeus appealed to the hundred-handed giants to use their strength and ferocity against the Titans.

Then the gods of Olympus and their allies set about the Titans with renewed fury. The sea boiled and the earth burned. Into the dust-storm of battle Zeus hurled his bolts of thunder and lightning and the hundred-handed giants sent a thick rain of stones on the heads of the enemy. The Titans were overwhelmed and defeated.

In triumph, Zeus had them bound in chains and thrown down to Tartarus, which lies so far under the earth that a falling anvil would take nine days to reach that prison region of dark and dank and cold. Zeus, the Cloud-Gatherer, condemned them to this fate. Poseidon walled them in and locked the gates of bronze. The hundred-handed giants, each with fifty watchful heads, kept guard over the fallen Titans. Of the Titans, Zeus spared only his mother Rhea, and her sister goddesses. And Atlas, leader in battle, strongest of all the Titans, he punished in a different way. Banished from Olympus, he was condemned to stand forever at the edge of the earth, supporting the high-curved sky on his mighty shoulders.

Zeus had overthrown the Titans, but his days were not yet free from struggle. Mother Earth, who had seen her elder children brought down by Zeus, now lay with Tartarus and brought forth Typhon, her youngest child. Huge, terrible and tireless, this son of Ge surpassed all other children of Earth in size and strength. He was so tall his head knocked the stars, and his arms extended from sunrise to sunset. From his winged shoulders writhed a hundred snake heads with eyes flashing fire. Upward from the waist he was shaped like a man, with a brutish head sunk in wild tangles of hair and beard. But instead of legs, there grew from the lower part of his body two great serpents which coiled and intertwined. Unspeakable sounds came from the multitude of his snaking heads. Sometimes they seemed like words that the gods might understand, then came the bellowing of a bull, or a lion's roar, or the cry of whelps, or hisses that whistled with a sinister echo through the hills.

Zeus took up arms against this monster, and Olympus itself shook under the onslaught. The whole earth trembled and the confusion was felt even in the land below, where Hades ruled over the dead and the Titans groaned in Tartarus. Zeus released his bolts and blasted the monster with thunder and lightning. Typhon's hundred snaking heads were scorched, and the monstrous body fell seared with heat, so that the ground around it melted. In victorious anger, Zeus hurled Typhon into Tartarus.

Some say, however, that the victory was not so easily accomplished. These tell how great Zeus put the monster to flight, but that at Mount Casius, in Syria, Typhon turned and stood at bay. Grappling at close quarters, Typhon wrenched the cruel sickle-shaped sword from his opponent's hand and cut the sinews from the hands and feet of Zeus. Then Typhon carried Zeus off to the Corycian cave in Cilicia—the cave of the Leather Sack where the winds were kept—and hid the severed sinews in a bearskin. The dragon Delphyne, half woman and half serpent, was set on guard.

The reign of Zeus was not so easily ended. Released and made whole by his brother gods, Zeus immediately flew up to heaven in a winged chariot, grasped his thunderbolts, and again set off after Typhon, following him tirelessly, hunting him down. The fight led them far and wide through the

## The origins of Zeus and Typhon

The story of Typhon is another of Hesiod's myths which seems to have come originally from further east. The Hittite people who created a great empire in Anatolia (modern Turkey) had a myth telling of a storm god who had to do battle with a fearsome dragon. The dragon defeated him and took away and hid his heart and eyes, just as Typhon took away the sinews of Zeus. Eventually the storm god got his heart and eyes back, defeated the dragon and ruled as king of the gods.

## Naming places

Pytho, where Zeus placed the stone Cronus had swallowed, became Delphi, the shrine of Apollo.

Delphi is situated in central Greece and Zeus was thought to have placed the stone there because it was in the exact centre—'the navel' it was called—of the world. Zeus found the centre by releasing two eagles at the same time, one from the eastern edge and the other from the western edge of the world. They met at Delphi. Another stone there, of conical shape, worshipped since the Mycenaean age, was thought to represent the actual 'navel'.

The name Mount Haemus would remind a Greek of the word *haima*, meaning blood. The detail in the story of Zeus and Typhon was probably included to explain the origin of the name. Similarly, many myths were told to explain the awe-inspiring nature of Mount Aetna, then an active volcano.

hills and valleys of Greece, from the southern coastlands to the crinkled mountains of the north. In distant Thrace, Typhon picked up a mountain and flung it at Zeus. But he was weak and bleeding. He missed his aim, and his blood falling on the mountain gave it the name Mount Haemus, which means 'Blood Mountain'.

At last the monster's strength and will were ended and he fled secretly to Sicily. But even there he could not escape the god. Zeus caught him and crushed him under Mount Aetna, which to this day still belches fire from the defeated monster.

# THE GODS AND GODDESSES OF OLYMPUS

## Zeus, Lord of Olympus

Zeus, Thunderer and Lord of the Bright Sky, came to power as had been foretold. The succession passed through the generations of the gods, and his immortal ancestors made way for him. To Zeus above all, men gave their homage, acknowledging his chief place among the gods. They honoured him with many names, and the peoples of mankind, recognizing his supremacy, vied with each other to claim the holy place of his birth.

The people of Arcadia say that when Rhea's time was come she went in the night to Mount Lycaeum, to the land where no shadows form, and there gave birth to the divine baby. Then she bathed him in the River Neda and handed him to Mother Earth, who carried the infant Zeus away to Lyktos in Crete, where he might be kept safe from the jealousy of his father Cronus.

The Cretans, on the contrary, say that Rhea flew straight to their land for the birth of her great son. And though they indignantly deny the Arcadians' claim, nonetheless they also quarrel among themselves as to the exact place of the god's birth. Such is the way of men, to compete for glory.

When the birth-pangs of the goddess began, she supported herself with her hands on the ground, and from the marks of her fingers the mountain brought forth spirits known as the Dactylae, which means 'the Fingers'. These spirits were also called the Curetes, or the Youths, and they were the armed guardians of the child. When Rhea was delivered of the baby, little Zeus was placed in a golden cradle and suspended in the air from the bough of a tree, so that Cronus could not find him: being neither on earth nor in heaven nor in the sea, the child was safe from all his spies. At the foot of the tree lay a golden dog, watchful, on guard. And when the infant cried, shaking the air with his divine lungs, the Curetes danced around him, singing and clashing their weapons, to drown out the wails and keep them from the ears of Cronus.

Zeus grew up in the solitude of his mountain retreat. The nymphs of the ash tree cared for him and the goat nymph Amaltheia was his nurse. The bees fed him with their honey and Amaltheia gave him her milk. In gratitude, Zeus took one of Amaltheia's horns and formed it into the horn of plenty, the famous Cornucopia, which gave an inexhaustible supply of food and drink. Later, Zeus placed the image of his nurse among the stars and there she still shines as Capricorn, the constellation of the Goat. Nor was this the end of her honours. When Zeus needed a cloak to give him invincible protection, he took a goatskin in memory of Amaltheia and it became his sacred aegis, a sign and symbol of his divinity.

His youth passed and Zeus came to maturity, a god full of power, ready to enter into his inheritance. When the long battles with the older generation were done, when the Titans and giants were overcome and father Cronus sent packing into his immortal dotage, Zeus surveyed his dominions. Supreme among gods, conqueror of Titans, lord of the universe, and yet even his divine will was not unlimited. Like everything that was, and is, he was compelled to operate within the rules of destiny. The Fates, born from Darkness and Night at the beginning of time, held each being, mortal and immortal, in their grip. Clotho, the first sister, spun the thread of destiny; Lachesis, the second, measured out the length; and Atropos, the smallest but most terrible of the three, snipped off with her shears the allotted portion. No man could live beyond his destined span. Not even Zeus could change what the Fates foretold.

The brothers of Zeus, Poseidon and Hades, also had rights, by virtue of their high birth as the elder sons of Cronus and Rhea. The three gods drew lots to divide the ancestral estate of the gods: Zeus drew the heavens as his portion, Poseidon the sea, and Hades the world below. On earth and on Olympus they exercised power in common, though Zeus was without doubt the greatest of the three.

Once his rule was established, Zeus began to look, as was only right and natural, for a partner in heaven. Some men say that Dione was his first consort, though the memory of her is only a faint echo from the distant age of our farthest ancestors. Perhaps she was a daughter of Oceanus, the god whose mighty river encircled the world; but more likely, she was a goddess of spring-waters and a source of oracles. Only in the ancient oak-groves of Dodona was she well remembered.

The old poets unite him first with Metis, whose name means Wisdom. When she conceived, Zeus grew afraid. Ge and Uranus told him this first child would be a daughter but that the second would be a son. And this son, they said, was destined to topple his father, just as Zeus himself had overthrown Cronus, and as Cronus had deposed Uranus. And as Cronus had consumed his children, so Zeus took Metis and swallowed her, to possess her wisdom and also to prevent even her first child from being born.

Great Zeus, however, was not content with one consort. Many were drawn to his bed so that he peopled the heavens with gods and spirits.

First came the Titan goddess Themis, who gave birth to Eunomia, Dice and Eirene—that is to say, Government, Justice and Peace. Then Eurynome lay with him, and she brought forth the Graces. After this Zeus mated with his sister Demeter, and their daughter was Persephone, the sad one later snatched down to the Underworld. Mnemosyne, another Titan goddess, became the mother of the nine Muses, those spirits who keep watch over the arts of men. Then Leto bore him twins, the god Apollo and the hunter goddess Artemis.

At last, Zeus made Hera his wife and consort, queen goddess of Olympus. The divine couple kept

## Aristocrats of Olympus

With the coming to power of Zeus and the other Olympians the world that the Greeks knew had, in their view, taken shape.

It was from the poems of Hesiod and Homer that the Greeks took their ideas about the gods and goddesses. But the two poets were very different in their personalities and their circumstances and they told the myths in ways that reflected this. Hesiod shaped the myths into poems that made sense of the world as it appeared to him living the hard life of a farmer in a countryside where all the wealth and power belonged to a few aristocrats.

Homer was no humble farmer, nor did he live as Hesiod did in the backward countryside of central Greece. Instead he lived among aristocrats of the brilliant civilization that had grown up in the cities founded by the Greeks on the islands and coast of the eastern Aegean. Life for the aristocrats was not harsh, nor were they in any danger of being oppressed by the rich and well-born, since they themselves were the rich and well-born. Homer's poems tell of the deeds of the heroes at the siege of Troy and he was interested in the Olympian gods because they were closely involved with the heroes and largely responsible for their achievements and misfortunes. For Homer the reign of Zeus is like the government of a group of unruly aristocrats. His Olympians have almost unlimited power to interfere in the affairs of mortals—to favour those they like, persecute those who have offended them, fall in love with and seduce or rape their daughters—when they are not seducing or raping the nymphs of the woods and streams. All this Homer refers to as if it were the most natural way for the gods to behave.

Hesiod's poems, too, describe promiscuous matings of gods and goddesses with mortals and with one another, but to him this is all part of the emergence of order out of heavenly confusion and strife. The triumph of Zeus, in particular, is the triumph of a great god concerned to see that there is justice on earth and punishment for aristocrats who take bribes in return for giving crooked (by which Hesiod means unjust) judgements.

state on Olympus, but there were sharp differences between them. Hera was jealous and Zeus still was not faithful. It was hard, if not impossible, for him to resist the darts of love, and many goddesses, spirits and also humans found themselves in his power. By Maia, daughter of the giant Atlas, he fathered Hermes, the divine messenger. And from Semele, daughter of the human Cadmus, came Dionysus, god of wine. Hera's own children were Hebe, Ares and Eileithyia—the goddess of youth, the god of war and the goddess of childbirth.

For all the power that he had won, and the great authority vested in him, Zeus did not reign easy on Olympus. Nor was he without challengers. His brothers and sisters, with his wife Hera among them, were restless and often resentful. They were slow to accept his authority and quick to oppose him, entering into the wickedness and the schemes of men, which set the gods at odds with one another.

Once, two giant sons of Poseidon tried to storm the mountain fortress of Olympus, planning to pile two smaller mountains, Pelion and Ossa, one on top of the other, like giant stepping stones. And even Zeus' closest family dared to plot his downfall. Hera, Poseidon and Athene—his wife, brother and daughter—made plans to bind him in chains. But Thetis, daughter of Nereus, saved him. She summoned to Olympus one of the hundred-handed giants, one of those whose monstrous strength had helped to subdue the Titans. He guarded Zeus with such frightening zeal that the conspirators slunk away in terror.

At the summit of Olympus, Zeus, the Most High, received the offerings of mankind. He was the father of gods and men. With thunderbolt and lightning flash in hand, he dealt justice and to the guilty, punishment. From him flowed order, safety and government, so that the poet was right to sing his universal praise: 'Lord of lords, most holy of the blessed, most perfect of the perfect, radiant Zeus.' Around his throne, eager to quarrel and fight, stirred the forceful and independent members of his family, the gods and goddesses of Olympus.

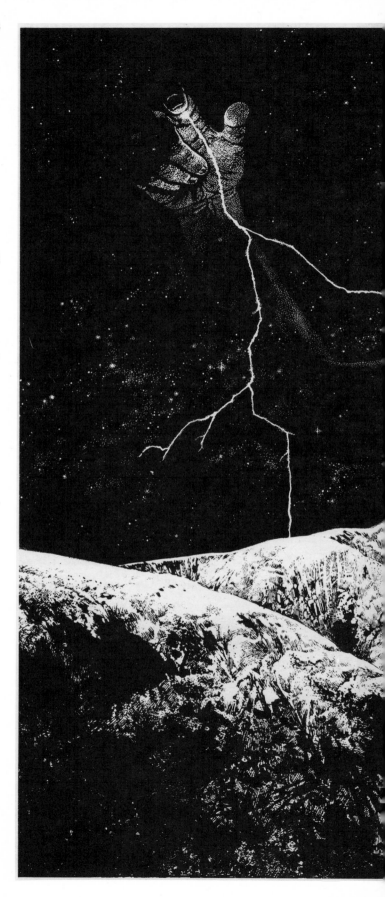

# Poseidon, god of the sea

Two gods, the sons of Cronus, were older than Zeus and shared with him the government of the world. Poseidon was the eldest, and when the estate of the gods was divided, he took the sea as his realm. He was the Earth-Shaker. From his golden palace, deep in the waters off Aegae, in Euboea, he agitated the swirling currents and whipped up the waves so that the ground trembled. The lesser gods of rivers and streams, and all the spirits of water obeyed him, for he was a stern master. When he appeared to men, he clutched his trident, the symbol of his power. Shaggy, sea-green locks fell in wild confusion around his surly face. Violent, sudden, and quick to anger, he made the gods apprehensive and struck fear into the hearts of men.

Some say that after his birth, Poseidon was not swallowed by his father, Cronus, with his younger brothers and sisters. These claim that Rhea hid him among a flock of sheep. Others say that she carried him to the Telchines, a people of the Underworld who practised secret arts on the island of Rhodes and forged his trident for him by their skills.

When Poseidon was ready to enter into his kingdom of the sea, he began to look for a wife who could live with him in his world of water. First, he sought out Thetis, one of the fifty Nereids, daughters of the ancient shape-changer, Nereus, 'the Old Man of the Sea'. But Thetis' child was fated to be greater than his father, and Poseidon let her be. Then he pursued another Nereid, Amphitrite, whom he saw dancing with her sisters on the island of Naxos. In his uncouth way he tried to ravish her, so that she fled to Atlas at the western edge of the world. Poseidon sent Delphinus, the dolphin, to plead for her return, and this Delphinus did with such success that Poseidon rewarded him with a place among the stars.

Amphitrite was a jealous wife and she had reason to be, for her husband, proud and violent in most things, was a wilful lover, as unfaithful as his brother Zeus. On one young rival, Scylla, Amphitrite took a fearful revenge. Throwing magic herbs into the girl's bath, she changed Scylla into a twelve-legged monster with six snarling heads in the form of dogs. Scylla, grown hideous and full of hate, made her home in a cave beside the narrow Straits of Messina. There, to spite the sea god, protector of mariners, she snapped and menaced all sailors who dared to pass that way.

Revenge and threats did little to cure Poseidon of his lusts. The winged horse Pegasus was his son, born from the head of the hideous gorgon Medusa. And in the form of a stallion himself, Poseidon fathered Demeter's son Arion, the black-maned horse as swift as the wind; and a daughter whose unmentionable name was known only to the initiates of the Mysteries, the rites and rituals of Demeter.

Although he was god of the sea, Poseidon continued to meddle on the land, sowing dissension and bitterness in cities and countries that honoured other gods. He tried to wrest Aegina from Zeus, Troezen from Athene, and Naxos from Dionysus. He laid claim to Corinth and even tried to gain the land of Attica. No dispute with Hera was ever moderate and when he tried to snatch Argolis from her, the contention grew so fierce that three powerful river gods were asked to judge between the two furious Olympians. When they decided in favour of Hera, Poseidon's revenge was swift: he called a curse upon the judges' river kingdoms so that in summer, they became as dry as dust, with not even a trickle of water flowing through their sandy beds. And so they remain to this day.

Equal in dignity to his brother Zeus, but inferior to him in power and authority, Poseidon was a rugged god whom men both respected and feared. Like the sea itself, his nature was moody, changeable, turbulent and dangerous. And as men approached the sea with caution, so they approached the god with prayers and many offerings, lest his notorious anger flare up and shake the world with quakes and floods and tidal waves.

## Who was Poseidon?

Poseidon has been something of a puzzle to the scholars. As well as being the god of the sea, he was the god of earthquakes, of freshwater springs (but not of rivers) and of horses. The sea, horses, freshwater springs and earthquakes do not obviously belong together. Connections of a sort can be found: two springs sacred to the Muses were supposed to have been made by the hoof of a horse; as god of the sea Poseidon drives across the waves on a horse-drawn chariot; earthquakes sometimes produce tidal waves. These, however, are all flimsy connections. A more persuasive theory is that Poseidon came to Greece with the Greek-speaking peoples in the Bronze Age and that he was then a god of the earth (his name may have meant 'husband of the earth' or 'lord of the earth'). Earthquakes (quite frequent in Greece) begin with rumblings from under the earth, and spring water gushes up from the earth.

The Greek-speaking peoples came originally, it is thought, from the steppes of Russia (or possibly the plains of northern Anatolia) where horses are important but the sea is not. A god of horses would therefore have been a major god. Greece, however, is a rugged land, less suited to horses and the sea is often a quicker way of going from one place to another than are the tracks across the mountains that divide them. So some of the invading Greeks took to the sea as traders, and others as pirates and sea-raiders, like the Vikings two thousand years later. The sea, now smooth and smiling now turbulent and dangerous, must be under the control of some god. Just how the god of springs and horses became that god is not obvious.

Poseidon's trident, in ancient Greece a weapon used by fishermen for spearing tuna fish, became a symbol of the rule of the seas.

# Hades, ruler of the Underworld

The third son of Cronus, the one who drew the Underworld as his lot, was the god known as Hades. To tell the truth, Hades was not a proper name, since it means only 'Invisible One'. It is best not to speak about matters of the dead, neither about the kingdom nor the god, but merely to give respectful homage and refer to the great god indirectly as the Invisible One or as Pluto, 'the Rich One', or Eubuleus, 'the Good Counsellor' or as Polydegmon, 'the Hospitable'.

The poets called the god Hades 'the Zeus of the Underworld', and others said that he resembled Zeus in all his person, except he did not possess the mighty thunderbolt. Hades was a severe and inexorable god in his land below the earth, meting out the pain and correction that the justice of his brother Zeus decreed. On earth, when men called for retribution against their fellows, they struck the ground and swore their oaths in the name of Hades.

Few escaped from his sad kingdom, for he was a watchful lord. Tied to his duty, he had little time to wander into the living world or up among the gods of Olympus. His knowledge of deeds done above was limited to what mankind told him in their prayers, or what he heard from the shades of the departed. And when he left his kingdom, he often went secretly, wearing the helmet of invisibility which the Cyclopes had made for him. As his title Pluto, the Rich One, implied, he owned all the jewels and precious metals that lay under the ground. But he owned nothing above, and the shrines of his worship, since men avoided his name, were few and far between.

Sometimes the needs of love drew him out of his gloomy realm. Once he chased the nymph Minthe in his chariot with the black horses, and would have ravished her had not Persephone intervened and transformed the nymph into the sweetsmelling plant called mint.

Long before this, however, Hades had set his

desire towards Persephone herself and plotted to
take her and make her his wife. Persephone, also
called Core or 'the Maiden', was the daughter of
Zeus and Demeter, and being a virgin of
extraordinary beauty, she was strictly guarded by
her mother on the island of Sicily. Hades fell in
love with Persephone and asked for her hand in
marriage; but Demeter was afraid to lose her
daughter to the bleak Underworld, and she
refused. Hades petitioned Zeus, the virgin's father,
but Zeus would not be swayed. Hating to displease
either his sister Demeter or his brother Hades, he
answered cunningly that he could neither give his
permission nor withhold it.

Hades, taking this as a sign that Zeus would not
interfere with his plans, decided to trap
Persephone and abduct her to his kingdom down
below. In this he was helped by Ge, the Earth. One
day, as Persephone was gathering flowers in the
fair field of Enna, she found a single white
narcissus placed there by Ge to grow among the
crocuses, violets, irises and hyacinths. As
Persephone reached to pick it, the earth gaped
open at her feet. Hades burst from the chasm in his
golden chariot, seized her and carried her away,
down, down to his darkest Underworld, far from
the sweet light of the sun.

When Persephone did not return to Olympus,
Demeter set out anxiously to find her daughter.
Lighting her way with two torches from the fires of
Aetna, she wandered through the world, searching
here and there in desperation. While she wandered
through the hills and valleys of the land, the crops
in the fields withered and the earth grew bare and
bleak; for nothing could grow when Demeter,
goddess of the corn and the fruits of the earth, was
preoccupied.

The trail was difficult and obscure. No-one could
tell her who had taken Persephone. No-one knew
where she was now held prisoner. Disguised as an
old woman, Demeter came to Eleusis, the kingdom
of Celeus and his wife Metaneira. There the
unknown goddess was welcomed with kindness
and offered food and rest. Queen Metaneira was so
impressed by this distinguished-looking old

woman that she invited her to be nurse to her son Demophoön. The parents knew nothing of Demeter's real nature. To them she was simply a sad woman who had lost her child and who would care for theirs as for her own. Demeter was grateful for their hospitality and she resolved to reward them by making the little boy immortal. Using her divine powers, she rubbed him with ambrosia and held him over the fire, to burn away mortality. Unhappily, at this moment Metaneira entered and, seeing her child held in the flames, screamed in panic. The spell was broken, Demophoön died, and Demeter, taking her godly form, rebuked Metaneira for her unlucky intervention. For penance, the goddess imposed certain duties and rituals on the land of Eleusis, but in return she taught her secrets to the people and initiated them into the practice of the Mysteries which, ever after, were celebrated in her name.

Demophoön was dead but Demeter took the older son, Triptolemus into her favour. For it was Triptolemus who at last gave her the information she had been searching for. He told her how he had been herding his flock of goats one day when suddenly the earth opened at their very feet. There was a rush of wind and a thud of hooves and a team of black horses whirled a golden chariot into the depths of the chasm. The face of the charioteer was hidden, but he held tightly to a beautiful girl and her cries of anguish echoed behind the galloping hooves.

Demeter knew at once whose chariot she had seen. No-one but Hades could control the wild, black horses of the Underworld. Since she could not herself compel the powerful Lord of the Dead to return her daughter, Demeter hurried to Olympus to negotiate with Zeus.

Zeus, now ashamed of his part in the affair, sent Iris and Hermes, the messengers of the gods, to try to reconcile the differences between the two great gods. Demeter insisted on Persephone's return and Hades grudgingly gave way, for the earth was becoming barren as Demeter still withheld the fruits of the harvest. But when agreement was reached, and Persephone was about to mount the

## Homer's Hades

The Greeks' ideas of what would happen to them when they died, and what had happened to their ancestors, were vague and contradictory, but so have been those of many peoples in the past and so are those of many of us today. This is another of those aspects of the destiny of human beings on which science sheds no light.

Homer, whose poems never ceased to influence most Greeks, depicted death as departure to a gloomy world below the earth. It is so gloomy that when Odysseus, while still alive, manages to visit it, he is told by the dead hero Achilles that he (Achilles) would rather be the servant of a poor man on earth than rule as King of All the Dead. When Odysseus tries in vain to embrace the ghost of his dead mother, Anticleia, she explains to him the fate of mortals when they die. Their bones and flesh, she says, dissolve for lack of sinews. Then the bones and flesh are consumed on the funeral pyre while the soul of the dead mortal flutters away like a departing dream.

In Homer's Hades, as Odysseus sees it, there are criminals undergoing eternal torments and there are heroes who had been stern judges in the world of the living; but these judges only judge disputes among the dead. The criminals undergoing punishment are all being punished for crimes of violence or deception against the gods. What is missing is any tribunal to pass judgement and inflict punishment on mortals who have committed crimes against other mortals during their lifetime. To some later Greeks this seemed unsatisfactory, and for this reason different stories were told by other poets in which rewards and punishments were distributed in the Kingdom of Hades in recompense for good and bad deeds committed in our world.

There is more about Greek views of the afterlife on page 94.

chariot for her return to the upper air, the gardener of Hades called out that she had picked and eaten the fruit of the pomegranate, the food of the dead. Hades smiled grimly for he knew that even the gods could not set aside the unchanging rules of the Underworld: no-one who eats the food of the dead may ever fully return to the world above and Persephone's small act had bound her irrevocably to Hades' kingdom. The gods, who could not annul her fate, could only arrange a compromise. So almost as soon as Demeter had once more clasped her daughter in her arms at Eleusis, she was forced to let her go again. For the compromise allowed Persephone only a portion of each year on earth with her mother. The rest of the time she was bound to her husband Hades as his queen. The Fates had decreed it, and the gods could only acknowledge the inevitable.

Then Demeter was satisfied and in the fields and forests of the world the wild flowers bloomed and the crops for the harvest began to grow once more. Only when the days grew shorter and the dark nights longer, did Persephone return to Hades. At this time, Demeter, goddess of fruitfulness, covered her face with her cloak and the earth grew bare and barren until Persephone should bring the spring again.

Since not even Zeus could part them, Hades and Persephone ruled together in the world below. Stern as always, he was the ungiving master over the shades of the departed. But she, his gracious consort, tempered his justice with her mercy.

# Ares, war god from the north

It is natural to respect the gods. The poets have taught us to be humble and submissive in the face of their greatness, and even those who made us shake with fear, such as Poseidon with his violence or grim, unforgiving Hades, received the reverence that is due to them from all mankind.

But one god on the heights of Olympus had no place in the hearts of men. Ares, god of war, was always a stranger to us, a cruel and murderous outsider who appeared some time in distant memory from the barbarian wilds of Thrace.

Ares was a son of Zeus and Hera. He was, if nothing else, a gigantic figure, as befits a god of war. When he lay on the ground, he covered some two hundred metres, and his roar when he was wounded was equal to the shouts of ten thousand men. But Zeus hated his son. He thought Ares was a destroyer of cities and a killer of men. Perhaps as a savage jest, Zeus blamed his son's nature on Hera, for he claimed that his consort had an ungovernable and headstrong temper. And perhaps it was Zeus himself who encouraged the tale that Ares was the child of Hera alone, conceived after she had plucked a magic flower.

Ares was god of wars of every kind, but above all he loved the violence and blood-letting of close combat. The rights and wrongs of warfare did not concern him, and he was likely to change sides at a whim. Nor was he an invincible champion in the field. Formidable Athene twice defeated him, contemptuously driving him wounded from the battle so that he rushed with whines and complaints to his father Zeus. The hero, Heracles, also sent him running to Olympus with his tail between his legs, in fear for his life. Even Otus and Ephialtes, riotous giants who grew at the rate of a fathom a year and who waged war on the gods, quite easily captured Ares. Mocking his strength and size, they imprisoned him in a bronze jar, full of helpless rage. He was only rescued thirteen months later when Hermes, the messenger god, pulled him from the jar half dead.

Detested by the gods, Ares was not greatly favoured by goddesses either. Aphrodite, out of perversity or wantonness, deceived her lame husband Hephaestus and lay with Ares. But that occasion ended badly. Hephaestus trapped them in a net, the lovers were shamed before the assembled gods and Ares slunk away in ridicule.

This, then, was the god whom all men hated. His children, like their father, were subject to violence and misery. Strife was his brother, his companions were Fear and Panic. Gods and men turned aside from him and gave him no honour.

## Ares and the Thracians

Religions in which many gods are worshipped are usually much more hospitable to the gods of other people than are Judaism, Islam or Christianity. The Greeks welcomed into their religion several gods worshipped by other peoples. The Romans went further and adopted all the Greek gods and goddessses, giving them the names of deities they had themselves been worshipping for many generations. Ares was called Mars by the Romans, who were proud to consider him as the founder of their nation, but to the Greeks he was rough and uncivilized. The Greeks were very proud of their own civilization and their own language. They referred to all peoples who did not speak Greek as 'barbarians' (people who spoke gibberish), even those with civilizations much older than their own.

If a Greek travelled by land outside mainland Greece the first barbarians he met would be the tribes who lived in Thrace. The Thracians amazed the Greeks because they were so very different from themselves. They had many wives whom they guarded jealously, but their unmarried daughters were allowed to sleep with anyone they liked. The Thracians tattooed themselves, they despised any occupation other than fighting and left their women to do all their farm work. They had too many children and were quite willing to sell some of them to the Greeks as slaves. They were very numerous and warlike but not at all powerful because they were divided into quarrelsome tribes ruled by quarrelsome kings. They had no cities, and they had strange funeral customs, rejoicing and merry-making when someone died, because they believed that death was a happy release from the misfortunes of life. All this was told by Herodotus. He also says that they worshipped Ares.

Scholars are not agreed as to whether the Greeks learned to worship Ares from the Thracians or merely thought that the Thracians' war god was so like Ares that he must be the same god. Whichever was the case, the myths make it clear that though he was the son of Zeus and Hera, yet, when not on Mount Olympus, or in the midst of some battle, Ares was to be found in Thrace.

# Radiant Apollo

Unlike Ares, radiant Apollo, son of Zeus and Leto, was universally loved and admired. Ares sent the unhappy shades of departed warriors to the Underworld; but all those things that made life virtuous, happy and secure for mankind received sympathy and encouragement from Apollo. God of prophecy and healing, guardian of navigation and father of colonies, patron of medicine and music, divine inventor of the lyre, Apollo was the most perfect and handsome of the sons of Zeus.

Apollo's birth was full of danger. Zeus loved Leto the Titaness, and she conceived. Carrying her unborn twins, she wandered from land to land, for jealous Hera had decreed that no place where the sun shone should receive her. To harrass her further, Hera sent the dragon Python from Delphi to follow her wherever she went, threatening her so that she could get no rest. It seemed there was no place where she could bring her children into the world, but, at last, a rocky little island called Delos agreed to accept her if she would bless it and make it the first shrine of her expected son. At that time the little island was floating without fixed position in the sea. Now Poseidon covered it with waves, so that the sun did not shine on it, and there, after nine days' labour, Leto brought forth the twin gods Artemis and Apollo. Eileithyia, goddess of childbirth, delivered the baby boy and wrapped him in linen. The goddess Themis fed him nectar and ambrosia. Immediately Apollo tasted the divine food, he burst his swaddling bands, grew to full size, and, bow and lyre in hand, climbed to the top of Mount Cynthus, bathing the barren island with holy light and making it fruitful. From that time on, the island of Delos was fixed forever in its place and, as Leto had promised, it became the first shrine of the new god.

Four days later, Apollo set out for Delphi to seek revenge on the dragon Python who had caused his mother so much misery. Some say he found Python coiled around a laurel tree and killed it in

its lair, but others believe it fled into the shrine of Ge and that Apollo followed it and killed it there, in the innermost sanctuary of the shrine. For this sacrilege, Ge made Apollo undergo purification and instituted the Pythian games, in honoured memory of the dragon. Forever after, Apollo was associated with holy Delphi.

Delphi was the very centre of the world, the *omphalos*, the navel of the earth. From most venerable times Delphi had been a place of oracles where Mother Earth made prophecies, giving voice to the future through her priestess, the Pythia. As the priestess sat on her sacred stool, the inspiration from the goddess came from a cleft in the ground and enveloped her, filling her mind with the knowledge and wisdom of Mother Earth herself.

After Apollo had completed his purification, Mother Earth forgave him and passed to him the power of the oracle at Delphi. As a sign of his new position, Apollo first began to build a temple. One old legend tells how the bees made him one of wax but Apollo's temple was a more glorious affair than that, built of good stone and carved and decorated by craftsmen in honour of the god. When the temple was ready, Apollo needed priests to serve it. Gazing out to sea one day, he saw a Cretan ship in the distance, making for Pylus on the western coast. Immediately he took the form of a huge dolphin, leaped from the water and spread himself on the deck. To the amazement of the terrified sailors, the dolphin guided the ship safely to Crisa, Delphi's harbour. There, reappearing in the form of a long-haired youth with a lyre, Apollo led the sailors to the temple and initiated them as his first priests. To quiet their fears, and demonstrate his powers, he made his first prophecy: 'Men will from this time onwards bring you rich gifts to hear the wisdom of the god. But if any of you becomes unjust, evil or arrogant, others will come and take your place by force.'

Rich or poor, all those who were troubled in mind or body came to Delphi, drawn by the fame of Apollo's oracle. The sick came to find a cure for all the diseases which afflicted them, for Apollo added the power of healing to that of prophecy.

Apollo could also delegate the gift of prophecy. Once, when he fell in love with Cassandra, daughter of King Priam of Troy, he gave the power to her. But Cassandra rejected him and, since the gift of a god could not be taken back, he punished her by adding a terrible condition to his gift. Her prophecies, though true, would never be believed, and her great power to see the future would always be unheeded and unvalued.

Some men say that while Apollo was still unborn, he travelled from the northern land of the Hyperboreans, and that his title was Lycius—the 'wolf god' who protects shepherds and their flocks with his skill at archery. Perhaps that was also where he learned the art of music, for music is the solace of shepherds and softens the loneliness of their solitary life. Very soon Apollo added music to the realm over which he ruled, and in this he defeated all challengers.

Pan was the first to test him in a musical contest. The chief of the judges gave the prize to Apollo, but Midas, king of Phrygia, disagreed. Apollo punished the king by giving him the ears of an ass. For a long time, Midas managed to conceal this ridiculous disability, hiding his ears beneath a Phrygian cap. But he could not keep his deformity a secret from his barber, who was sworn to secrecy, on pain of instant death. The barber was a garrulous fellow and found it extremely difficult to keep the information to himself. At last, unable to hold in his words any longer, he dug a hole and whispered the extraordinary news into the ground. The barber's relief did not last long for a clump of reeds soon grew up on the spot and knew the secret whispered to the earth. And when the breeze rustled through them, they sighed into the air: 'King Midas has ass's ears,' for everyone to hear. King Midas, furious at being made the laughing-stock of his country, condemned the barber to death.

Apollo was very severe with those foolish enough to challenge his musical pre-eminence, as the satyr Marsyas also discovered. By accident, Marsyas picked up a flute which Athene had thrown away. The flute was full of the music of the goddess and as soon as Marsyas played it, it made the most bewitching sounds, so that people cried out that even Apollo and his lyre could not make better music. Apollo was displeased and a contest was arranged with the nine Muses as the judges. Foolishly, Marsyas agreed, although the conditions were most severe: the winner could do whatever he wished with the loser.

At first, the Muses could not separate the skill of the contestants. Athene's flute sounded as beautiful as Apollo's lyre. Then Apollo challenged Marsyas to play and sing at the same time which, of course, no flute-player could do. In triumph, Apollo took his lyre once more, singing hymns of glory to the gods of Olympus; and the nine Muses, marvelling at his skill, judged him the winner.

## Apollo, Delphi and its prophecies

Apollo has surprised the scholars. In Victorian times he was thought of as the most Greek of Greek gods: a god of serene wisdom, moderation, and the disciplined arts of poetry and music, in which inspiration is controlled by the laws of rhythm and harmony. Yet scholars have now decided that Apollo was not, in origin, a Greek god at all but was adopted by the Greeks from some foreign people, probably from the Lycians, in Anatolia.

From the seventh to the fourth centuries B C Apollo's most important role for the Greeks was as the god of prophecy and his most important shrine was at Delphi where he inspired his priestess to prophesy the future. Often the shrine was visited by private individuals who wanted to know what was best for them to do in some personal matter, but sometimes the visitors were officials sent by the government of a Greek state, or even by foreign rulers. Delphi's priestesses had a great reputation in the seventh and sixth centuries B C for giving wise and statesmanlike answers. They helped the Greeks to solve their serious overpopulation problem by enouraging them to send out settlers to places around the Mediterranean coast. Delphi's reputation for good advice even survived a bad mistake at the beginning of the fifth century BC. When consulted by the Athenians on how they might best resist the impending Persian invasion, the priestess's answer implied that they had no hope of success. The Athenians, however, were determined to resist, so they asked again and were told that only wooden walls would save them. Their resourceful leader said that 'wooden walls' meant their fleet, and so persuaded the Athenians to resist the invasion by

sea, as he always intended they should. The result was victory in the great sea battle of Salamis.

The priestess' answers were often ambiguous, and from time to time kings or politicians took what they thought was her advice and came to disaster. When they complained they were told they had misinterpreted what she had said. Obviously it was important to ask the right question and to study the answer carefully if you wanted to make good use of Apollo's oracle.

Whereas the Greek sculptors and vase painters made Zeus and Poseidon in the image of bearded, awe-inspiring men in the prime of life, Apollo was conceived as the essence of youthful male beauty. In a famous carving on the temple of Zeus at Olympia (where the Olympic games were held) he appears as a strikingly handsome, athletic young man with serene, strong, yet sensitive, features. He is shown calmly directing a mythical battle fought by humans against centaurs—savage creatures, half human, half horse. Apollo is supporting civilized human beings against half humans made bestial by lust and drunkenness.

Carved at the entrance to Apollo's temple at Delphi was the motto *meden agan* which means 'nothing too much' or 'moderation in all things'. Also carved on the temple was the motto *gnothi seauton* which means 'know thyself' and was a reminder to those who came to Delphi that, however important they thought themselves, by comparison with the immortal gods they were weak and insignificant and unable to escape death whenever it was decreed for them. In time some Greeks came to interpret the motto as meaning that they should look searchingly into their own characters and take note of their strengths and weaknesses.

Success was not enough for Apollo, who took a cruel revenge on Marsyas. Since he could now do what he liked with the satyr, he had him flayed alive and his skin fixed to a plane tree by the river which now bears his name as a warning to others who might dare to challenge him. For Apollo, though the most dazzling of the gods, was dangerous to cross and terrible in his anger.

Once even Zeus aroused his furious wrath. Apollo had a favoured son, Asclepius, who had learned the arts of healing from his father and from Cheiron, wisest of all the Centaurs. Honoured by mankind for his skill in medicine, he dared to defy great Zeus and the Fates and raised some humans from the dead. Hades, angry to be deprived of subjects for his realm, complained to Zeus and Asclepius was punished for his presumption: Zeus struck him down to the Underworld with a thunderbolt. Apollo raged at the loss of his son. Too afraid to attack Zeus directly, he killed instead the Cyclops who had made the thunderbolt.

Apollo, like most of the gods, had various fortunes in love. He did not marry but pursued many nymphs and mortals, not always with happy results. One who escaped was Daphne, a river nymph who fled from him in fright. As she ran, she prayed to Mother Earth to save her and Ge turned her into a laurel tree, a tree forever after sacred to Apollo. Marpessa, a human girl, rejected him, fearing that he would leave her, a mere mortal, when she grew old. Dryope, a wood nymph, bore his son and served Apollo as his priestess until her companions spirited her away, leaving a poplar standing in her place. Some say the Corybantes were his children, those dervishes who practised the magic rituals of the dance.

Anger or frustrated love might make Apollo cruel or unjust, but he was still the darling of the gods. For they saw that in him were best combined all the qualities of heart and intelligence which nourished the life of mankind. When Apollo appeared in the assembly on Olympus, all the gods rose from their seats. Handing his bow and quiver to his mother, Leto, Apollo took his place, most honoured in that divine congregation.

# Hephaestus, the craftsman's god

Apollo, so perfect in face and body, easily won admiration, for our peoples always searched out and applauded all things beautiful in shape or form. But we were never quite sure about Hephaestus, the lame god with the crippled legs. He was so ugly and so badly formed. Some say he came from the east, from the lands of volcanic fire and sulphurous gases. And it is true that we have always known him as the miraculous craftsman, the divine smith, and the god of fire. When the blaze on the hearth jumps and crackles, men say, 'Hephaestus laughs'.

The oldest poets report that Hephaestus was the son of Hera alone. Others say that Zeus and Hera were his parents. Whatever is the truth of this, it is certain that Hera was disgusted by her crippled baby and threw him out of heaven. He fell tumbling to the sea where Thetis and Eurynome, daughters of Nereus, took pity on him and saved him. For nine years he lived with them beneath the sea, learning and perfecting his craft. But he did not forget his mother's cruelty. When he was skilled in all the craftsmen's arts, he made a golden chair and sent it to Hera as a gift. Hera accepted gratefully but when she sat down on the chair, it seized her and would not let her go. Not even the gods could free her. Ares came to plead for her, but Hephaestus drove him away with lighted torches. She was not released until Dionysus, god of wine, befuddled Hephaestus and persuaded the tipsy god to be reconciled to his mother.

Work at the forge gave Hephaestus the shoulders of a giant, but his lameness made him clumsy in movement, and his nature was abrupt and dour. He became the butt of the gods. On Olympus, they made him the victim of their jokes and laughed heartily at his awkward antics. Hard-working and preoccupied by his many projects, he also had little time for the sport of love. Yet by one of the ironies of heaven, he married Aphrodite, the goddess of love.

## Craftsmen and aristocrats

It is characteristic of the aristocratic society in which Homer lived that the god of technology should be an object of friendly ridicule among the other gods. Not that Homer despises skill in handicrafts. His hero Odysseus can turn his hand to making a raft, or even a bed, for himself, but then Odysseus is an aristocratic warrior who can also wrestle, box and throw the discus. The professional craftsmen who spent all their days in a workshop as leatherworkers or potters, or like Hephaestus as metalworkers beside their forges, could not become gentlemen because they did not have the leisure to cultivate their bodies through athletics and dance, nor their minds through poetry, song and the playing of musical instruments.

This low opinion of craftsmen persisted in aristocratic circles long after the age of Homer, at least until the end of the fourth century BC. So Hephaestus, though admired and worshipped for his technological achievements, was never a glamorous god like Apollo nor was he a god to be feared for awesome and unpredictable displays of power, like Zeus with his thunderbolts or Poseidon with the trident with which he stirred up or calmed the sea. For Athenians, however, the export of craftsmen's products was essential to pay for the import of grain (without which they would starve); so they built a fine temple to Hephaestus overlooking the main city square and close to the workshops of the metalworkers — and sometimes they called themselves 'the children of Hephaestus' because Erichthonius, the son of Hephaestus, had become their king and because they knew more about technology than any other Greeks.

Perhaps one of the more surprising things about the craftsmen of Athens, the stonemasons in particular, was that they worked side by side with (and sometimes under the supervision of) both foreigners and slaves, and all were paid equally. The only difference was that the slave's wage belonged not to him but to his master.

Hephaestus was first and foremost the craftsman god, the lord of fire, industriously forging all kinds of metal. The wonderful and beautiful objects made by him graced both heaven and earth. He constructed the bronze giant Talos, and Europa's brazen dogs. He made the bulls with feet of brass which Jason set to the plough, and the gold and silver dogs which guarded the house of Alcinous. He made the sickle of Demeter, the arrows of Apollo and Artemis, the gold cup of Helius the sun god and the sword of Perseus. It is said also that he made the aegis of Zeus. And for warriors on earth, he made a sceptre for Agamemnon, and armour for both Achilles and Diomedes in the Trojan war. Of these wonders there will be more to tell.

Idle gods on Olympus, whose days were often given to feasting and games, looked down on the hard-working smith sweating over his white-hot fires. But wherever men were busy Hephaestus received their offerings, and in inventive lands like Attica, he was held in high esteem, above many a more attractive but lazier god.

# Hermes, the messenger of the gods

Everyone knew Hermes. He was the youngest of the gods on Olympus, not very grand or powerful, but as familiar as a feature on the landscape — a well-loved hill, or a vigorous and indomitable tree. He was the god who reminded human beings most of themselves. Busy, cheerful and inquisitive, Hermes bustled about the affairs of all the world. And when they noticed him, men smiled and made him welcome.

Hermes was the child of Zeus and Maia, daughter of Atlas. Zeus visited her secretly in the night and she gave birth to the boy in a cave on Mount Cyllene in Arcadia. From the first, Hermes was an extraordinary child. On the very morning of his birth he rose from his cradle and went out to look at the world. There he saw a tortoise crawling through the grass and at once saw how he could invent a new musical instrument. He killed the tortoise, took its shell and tied strings across it to make the first lyre. Then he set out to explore further. Soon he came to a grassy plain where a herd of Apollo's cattle were grazing peacefully. Hermes decided to steal fifty cows, but to falsify the trail he drove them backwards and followed backwards himself in shoes he improvised from bark and twigs. By nightfall he had reached the River Alpheius. There he made a fire by rubbing laurel sticks together, slaughtered two of the animals and made a sacrifice in the proper ritual manner. He hid the remaining cattle in an olive grove and carefully retraced his steps. By the next morning he was back in the cave, tucked up in his cradle as if nothing had happened.

When Apollo came to inspect his cattle he was furious to find that fifty were missing. He searched in vain for traces of the thief and only found the culprit when an old countryman explained the trick of backward steps. By the time he reached the cave where Hermes lay, his rage was fierce. But little Hermes was unmoved, answering the god with great impudence. 'Why,' said the child in the cradle, 'how can I be the thief? I'm too young even to know what a cow is.'

Apollo was not satisfied and, taking him firmly by the hand, led him off to the court of Zeus. Maia, naturally, was afraid for her son, but Hermes went with cheerful confidence. 'Don't worry, mother,' he assured her. 'I mean to enter the assembly of the gods and all this follows my plan.'

When Apollo appeared on Olympus, leading the unrepentant Hermes, Zeus was vastly amused by the impudence of the young thief. He laughed and advised the half-brothers to make up their differences. Hermes gave back the hidden cattle and offered Apollo the newly made lyre in return for the two beasts that had been slaughtered. And all was well. Indeed, Apollo now took a liking to the enterprising young god and spoke up for him before Father Zeus. Apollo was a successful advocate and Zeus was pleased to welcome Hermes to Olympus, making him the herald and messenger of the gods, the overseer of roads and travellers, the protector of commerce, the go-between in all the regions of the world, and the

guide of souls on the way to Hades' kingdom. Zeus gave him the broad hat and the winged sandals and the herald's staff of his office. The only things that the greatest of the gods could not give him were eloquence and knavery, for these Hermes already had and it was these that made him naturally the patron god of thieves.

Now that he was so friendly with Hermes, Apollo even allowed him to learn a little of the art of divination. He learned to prophesy with pebbles in water, and Hermes himself invented a way of divination by throwing knuckle-bones. But wise Apollo was careful not to let him see too far or too much. For that was the trouble with Hermes. He was so quick and ingenious one never knew when he would stop. It was said that he invented, or helped to invent, the alphabet and astronomy, weights and measures, and musical scales. He presided over boxing matches and the games of the gymnasium. It was he who first began the cultivation of olive trees. He was so various and mercurial it was best to keep an eye on him.

Hermes was always inclined to go too far. When Zeus ordered Hermes to release Io, whom jealous Hera had changed into a cow under the guard of hundred-eyed Argus, Hermes lulled Argus to sleep with the music of the lyre, then cut out his eyes. For this, he earned the displeasure of the gods. Taken before the gods of Olympus, Hermes was acquitted of murder, but the angry gods threw at him the pebbles with which they voted, and these piles of stones can still be seen by the roads, which were also in Hermes' care.

Hermes was an amorous god, as may be expected of one so popular and confident. He chased many, caught many, and fathered many children. Hermaphroditus, the creature of both sexes, was his child with Aphrodite. Autolycus, most cunning of thieves, was Hermes' son as was the shepherd Daphnis, later transformed into the stone at Cephalenitanum.

All their lives men took comfort from Hermes. He kept them safe on the road, soothed their weariness with music, encouraged in them the spirit of commerce and enterprise. They liked his energy and humour, and when he was tricky or dishonest, as he sometimes was, they forgave him, because he was at heart a good fellow. And at the end, when the people of this world slipped out of life, it was Hermes who took them by the hand and led them on the dark journey to the Underworld.

### The god of good luck

Hermes was, among other things, the god who brought good luck. A Hermaion was a stroke of good luck, a 'wind-fall' — in other words a gift of Hermes. Owners of houses in Athens erected outside their doors a pillar topped by the head of Hermes (they called it a 'herm') to keep away bad luck, just as, in the days when discarded horseshoes were easy to come by, householders in Britain used to nail up horseshoes over their front doors with the same idea.

As the messenger of Zeus, Hermes was of necessity a great traveller, so he was naturally considered to be the patron god of travellers. Tracks through the countryside were marked by a large stone surrounded by a pile of smaller ones. These were also called 'herms'. Travellers would add their own stone to the pile as they passed, in acknowledgement of the presence of Hermes. So today, whenever a walker comes to the top of a hill and drops a stone onto the little pile begun by other walkers, he or she is (probably unknowingly) paying a tribute to Hermes.

Because of the tricks he played, as an infant, on his half-brother Apollo, Hermes was also the patron god of thieves and tricksters. His son Autolycus was the most successful thief of all time, so when Shakespeare needed a name for a thief and trickster in his play *The Winter's Tale*, he called him Autolycus. In Greek mythology Autolycus is the grandfather of Odysseus, who inherited from him the ability to talk or trick his way out of some very difficult situations.

In modern times, Hermes is better known by his Roman name of Mercury. With his winged helmet and sandals and herald's wand he is widely used as a symbol of speed and communications.

# Hestia, goddess of hearth and home

The gods took their place on the summit of Olympus. They were joined by six goddesses, consorts and fellow rulers who recognized the divine kingship of Zeus, the Thunderer.

Modest Hestia was first among the goddesses, the eldest daughter of Cronus and Rhea. When the battles of heaven were finished, and the Titans sent defeated to their fate, Hestia swore by Zeus' head that she would remain a virgin forever. Zeus heard her oath and her wish was granted, though both Poseidon and Apollo were suitors for her hand. But she had no time for the strife of heaven or the strife of the sexes. She found her place by the hearth and rested there content. She was the conciliator, and in recognition of her role as peacemaker Zeus granted her the first victim in every sacrifice.

The great affairs of the world passed her by. The poets felt no need to say much about her because to them she was always present as Hestia, goddess of the hearth. She was the centre and the cause of well-being in the home of every family, and the hearth-fire burned for her. When the troubles of the world heaped up, and fame and glory meant nothing more, then all people turned to Hestia.

# Hera, Queen of Heaven

Hera never found on Olympus that peace which settled around her sister Hestia. Perpetually, Hera struggled against her husband Zeus. Her days were careworn in her own defence and in defence of women.

Hera was a daughter of Cronus and Rhea and she was born into conflict. When tumult began in heaven, caused by the tyranny of Cronus against his children and by the subsequent revolt of Zeus, Rhea sent Hera to a place of safety with Tethys and Oceanus, and these two raised her. When she was grown up, her stately beauty caught the eye of her brother Zeus, and that meant yet more trouble.

Many tales were told of the stormy wooing that led to the 'holy marriage' of Zeus and Hera. Some say Zeus pursued her in the form of a cuckoo. When Hera was wandering in the mountains, Zeus caused a fierce tempest and then, as a trembling cuckoo, took refuge in her lap. Hera comforted the frightened bird beneath her robe, but the god assumed his proper person and tried to ravish her. But the people of Boeotia claim that Zeus first saw Hera in all her beauty on the island of Euboea and abducted her to Mount Cithaeron. Her nurse came looking for Hera, but the mountain spirit stopped her, saying that Zeus was far away in the arms of Leto. Others say that Zeus and Hera were already quarrelling on Cithaeron. To spite her, Zeus let it be known that he was about to marry another. A log of wood was carved into her form and dressed in bridal clothes. When Hera saw this wedding procession, she rushed out in jealous consternation, but when the log was unveiled, for once everything ended in laughter and good spirits.

Others, however, say that it was Hera who chased Zeus, borrowing the magic girdle of Aphrodite as a love charm. Many places vied for the honour of this wedding. The Euboeans pointed out to strangers a remote island cave. The Cretans favoured a spot by the River Theres, near Cnossus. Others thought that the two gods, because they were brother and sister, deceived their elders and went secretly to their marriage bed.

Still others placed the marriage at Zeus' palace in the realm of Oceanus, by the far shores of the western seas. Here the gods brought their wedding gifts, among them an apple tree with fruits of gold, the gift of Mother Earth. Hera planted the tree there, in the garden of the gods, setting the daughters of Atlas, the Hesperides, to care for it and a dragon to watch and guard them all.

No-one could doubt the importance of this wedding. The coming together of the divine couple was a momentous event in the history of Olympus. The people of Samos were so overcome by the majesty of the occasion that they claimed for their island the consummation of the marriage which lasted, with pardonable enthusiasm, for three hundred years.

But married happiness did not last. First, Hera had to contend with her husband's spectacular infidelity. He himself once drew up for her a partial list of his loves. There was Danaë, and Ixion's wife, and Europa, daughter of Agenor, and Semele, and Alcmene, and Demeter, and Leto. Nor did that complete the list. As a result of this philandering, bad blood arose between Zeus and Hera. He was rough and brutal and even threatened her with his thunderbolts. She nagged him and schemed against him, forever taking one side when he favoured the other.

At one point, bitterness between the divine pair broke into open rebellion. Hera plotted with other gods of Olympus to depose Zeus. For a while it seemed that they would triumph, until Thetis summoned the hundred-handed giant Briareus to come and save Zeus. For this revolt, Zeus punished his wife severely. She was suspended from heaven in chains, with anvils tied to her feet, and she was not freed until she swore never again to rebel against the Father of Heaven.

Perhaps it was from this time that things went better between them. They had their softer moments, and Hephaestus, Ares, Hebe and Eileithyia were born of their union. The poet has pictured them in their loving moments, in each other's arms on Mount Ida, lying peacefully on a bed of hyacinths and covered by a golden cloud.

Despite her anger and unhappiness at Zeus' infidelity, Hera was still Zeus' wife and consort, co-regent of heaven, and she had the power and dignity proper to her position. Those who crossed her were subject to her notorious displeasure. She drove Heracles and Athamas mad, so that they killed their children. She persecuted Io with gadflies until she, too, went mad. Even the gods did not escape her, for she sent Dionysus wandering in a frenzy over all the eastern world. Her powers were great, but her responsibilities were also considerable. The weather obeyed her and the bird of rain, the cuckoo, was sacred to her, perhaps because of Zeus' old disguise. She raised the storm that drove King Agamemnon back to his homeland after the fall of Troy. But her chief care was the well-being of women, to uphold and protect them in all the troubles of daily and married life, and to make sure they received due respect and reward from their husbands who were, too often, as faithless and uncaring as her own.

For all this, she was worshipped by both men and women as a mighty goddess.

## Demeter, goddess of the harvest

Punishment and retribution come from the hands of the gods. Their rage is terrible and their justice severe. But the goddesses have another, softer aspect. It is in their nature to foster and conserve.

Demeter, third of the daughters of Cronus and Rhea, was the goddess of the soil. In particular, she watched over the cornfield and the yearly gathering of the harvest. But everything that grew also came under her care, and those who violated nature had reason to fear her, as Erysichthon of Thessaly found to his cost. Needing timber to make a banqueting hall, he took his axe to a sacred grove, a grove dedicated to Demeter herself. The goddess was angry. Her trees were being cut down and some say a nymph was killed in the felling. But Demeter's nature was mild. Instead of punishing the rogue immediately, she took on the person of the priestess of the grove and merely warned Erysichthon against foolish impiety. But he ignored her warning, preferring rather to feast than to respect the goddess. So she condemned him to perpetual hunger. He ate and ate, yet he was never satisfied and grew thinner and thinner. His ravenous appetite consumed all his wealth until at last he was reduced to beggary, grubbing for garbage in the road.

All the wealth of nature was in Demeter's gift. In an early moment of passion she had made love to the Titan Iasius, lying with him in a thriceploughed field. The child of this union was Plutus, whose name means 'Riches', in this case the riches of the earth. Plutus spread his benefits among mankind,

being welcomed by all farmers and cultivators. But Zeus, who saw the lovers coming from the field, was furious that the Titan should touch his sister and he struck Iasius dead with a lightning-bolt.

Perhaps it was jealousy that made Zeus so fierce against Iasius. For Demeter, though she never married, had a gentle and bountiful character that made the gods desire her. Poseidon pursued her and when she turned herself into a mare to escape him, he took advantage of her animal form, became a stallion and covered her. Zeus also lusted after his sister Demeter, and Persephone, called Core, was his daughter. The rape of the young and beautiful Persephone by Hades, grim god of the Underworld, caused the enduring sadness of Demeter's life.

Mankind gave thanks to Demeter for the fruits of the earth. The first loaf made from the new harvest was dedicated to her. But she was more than simply the provider. Her patient powers to comfort and nourish gave her the title 'Thesmophorus', she who laid down laws and customs, keeping the people in peace and security. Unmarried herself, she watched over the household; and the arrival of children, as important to the world as any harvest, was another of her gifts of happiness.

## Athene, the wise goddess

In every land, the powerful exalt their own gods, and this was the case with the people of Athens. No deity had more praise from the poets of that city than grey-eyed Athene, patron goddess of Athens, defender of the walls, and goddess of all forms of practical wisdom.

When Metis, the mother of Athene, was pregnant with Zeus' child, he swallowed her because he feared the challenge of a son. But Metis had conceived a daughter. Later, as Zeus was walking by Lake Triton, he was gripped by a headache so painful that he roared out towards heaven. Hermes heard him and knew the cause of this disturbance. It was the child of Metis struggling to be born. Hermes persuaded

Hephaestus to take an axe and strike open Zeus' skull, from which emerged the stern figure of Athene. The grey-eyed goddess sprang forth fully armed and with her spear poised, an alarming figure to both gods and men; for she it was who fanned the heat of battle and took pleasure in the passion and the din of war.

Athene's birth was always mysterious and not all are satisfied with this wondrous account. Some say Brontes the Cyclops fathered Athene. Others say her birthplace was in Africa, by Lake Tritonis in Libya, where she was found and fostered by the nymphs. Still others claimed her father to be a certain giant called Pallas, from whom she took her familiar name of Pallas Athene.

From the beginning it was certain that Athene was a goddess to inspire awe and trembling. At her birth, when she leaped from her father's head, she sounded her war-cry and shook her spear to such effect that the whole world shuddered and the sun stood still. The children of the sun Hyperion hurried to placate her with a sacrifice on the island of Rhodes. In their haste they forgot the fire and ever since, the people of Rhodes have offered sacrifice without fire, which Athene has not spurned, for she has granted the craftsmen of the island the ability to make statues which seem alive.

All mankind recognized Athene as the most just and upright of the Olympians, but her very power made her dangerous to the unwary. Some say the name Pallas Athene came not from a father but from a girl companion of her youth called Pallas, with whom she practised the arts of war. One day, when the contest became a little heated, Zeus interposed his aegis to save his daughter from Pallas' blow. Momentarily distracted, Pallas did not see Athene's answering thrust, which killed her. In sorrow, Athene made an image of Pallas, the Palladium, a potent emblem which gave Athene's own protection to those who held it.

Another who challenged Athene's skill and suffered for it, was Arachne, a Lydian weaver, who boasted that she was more skilful than Athene herself. The goddess took up the challenge. As a warning to the mortal she wove a cloth whose pattern told the story of those who displeased the gods and were punished. But Arachne took no notice and wove a wonderful but scandalous tale of the loves of the gods. For this presumption, Arachne was beaten so severely that she hanged herself. Athene, relenting, saved her from death but turned her into a spider, so that she could weave her web with as much skill as she liked but without insult to the gods.

Formidable in everything, Athene was invincible in battle, borrowing from her doting father Zeus not only his warlike power but even, from time to time, his arms and armour. Twice she drove Ares, god of war, from the battlefield. But unlike the bully Ares she fought in the cause of just wars and in defence against aggression. The olive branch, which was her plant, became the symbol of peace after battle. Her first task was to encourage the inventions of mankind, to create rather than to destroy. She was the goddess of all craftsmen and builders and those with skilful hands. She made the soul of Pandora, the first of mortal women, whom Zeus created. She invented ploughing and spinning and weaving. She was the first to tame horses and showed the hero Bellerophon how to calm the immortal winged horse, Pegasus. She taught Epeius the skill to make the wooden horse that brought about the downfall of Troy. She helped to construct the Argonauts' ship and instilled in the crew the seamanship that steered them past the dangers of their journey.

Goddess of all practical crafts, Athene was also a patron of pottery, dance and music. She was the first to make earthenware pots. She shared the honour of devising the Pyrrhic dance, and she invented the trumpet and the flute.

Athene always bore the title 'Parthenos', the Virgin, and so she remained, for she seemed in her stately glory beyond the aspirations even of the gods. Hephaestus, the lame smith among the gods, tried to force her, but she fought off her unwanted lover. Thus Athene never had any children. But when Mother Earth gave birth to Hephaestus' son, Erichthonius, and would not keep him, she gave the baby to Athene, who hid the child in a chest. She took the chest to Athens and placed it for safekeeping with the three daughters of Cecrops, a creature who was half man, half serpent and the first king of Athens.

The daughters were strictly charged never to look in the chest. But Aglauros, the eldest, overcome by curiosity, raised the lid and showed the contents to one of her sisters. What they saw, no-one knows. Perhaps a child in the midst of snakes, perhaps one who was himself half human and half snake. In any case, the sight drove the three sisters mad so that they jumped from the rock of the Acropolis. While these events were happening, Athene was toiling towards the city with a gigantic stone to use in the fortifications. A crow brought her the news, and, when she heard it, she was so enraged that she dropped the stone and cursed the crow for bearing such a message. The stone became the hill called Lycabettus while the crow was changed in colour from white to an unlucky black.

But the people of Athens made amends. She had won the city and the surrounding land of Attica in a contest with Poseidon, to see which god could give the greater benefit. Poseidon, with a blow of his trident, had brought forth a salt-water spring. But Athene had caused an olive tree to grow on the Acropolis, and her great gift to agriculture won the day. Erichthonius grew up to become king of Athens and instituted the resplendent worship that the people offered to their patron goddess. And Athene did not forget her city. In the court of the Areopagus she took her place among the citizens, giving her casting vote in justice and compassion on the side of mercy.

# Artemis, the virgin huntress

The gods were often unpredictable and violent, but there were goddesses who were also dangerous. Chaste Artemis, goddess of hunting, rejoiced in her title of 'Lady of the Wild Beasts', and in her nature she showed some of the cold ferocity of the animals she governed. When she let fly her arrows, her aim was as deadly as Apollo's.

The divine twins Artemis and Apollo were the children of Zeus and Leto. When Leto was pregnant, jealous Hera gave her no peace and Leto could find no place to rest. At last, Delos accepted her and she gave birth clutching a palm tree for support. Artemis emerged from the womb first and she was so forward in development that she was able to assist at the delivery of her twin brother. Ever after, she was one of the goddesses of childbirth.

Both the twin gods were extremely precocious. At the age of three Artemis demanded, and received, certain presents from her father Zeus. Among these gifts were eternal virginity, the freedom of all wild places, and a bow and arrows equal to Apollo's weapons. Attended by young maidens, none of whom was ever more than nine years old, Artemis was sent by Hephaestus to the workshops of the Cyclopes, where Brontes made her a silver bow. In return, she granted the Cyclopes the first prey struck by her arrow. Then, to complete the equipment she needed for the hunt, she went on to Arcadia and received from the nature god Pan ten fierce dogs, big enough to bring down a wounded lion and fast enough to catch the swiftest running deer.

With weapons, dogs and hunting skill, Artemis was an implacable opponent. At first, she had favoured Orion of Boeotia, for they were both great hunters. But Orion offended the gods with his lust. He also boasted of his hunting prowess, threatening to empty the whole world of wild beasts. This presumption was too much for the twin gods Apollo and Artemis. Apollo sent a giant scorpion to attack Orion. And when Orion tried to escape by swimming, the god mischievously dared Artemis that she could not hit the target of Orion's head, bobbing far away above the waves. Artemis' arrow pierced him through the skull. But some say that Artemis shot Orion because he dared to challenge her at throwing the discus. Perhaps in repentance for the way Apollo had tempted her to misuse her skill, Artemis set her victim among the stars as the constellation Orion, forever pursued across the heavens by the Scorpion.

The beautiful Callisto was another who fell to Artemis' arrow. When Callisto and Zeus became lovers, Hera, jealous as usual, changed Callisto into a bear, drove her out on to the mountainside, and then sent Artemis in pursuit. It was a death sentence on the unlucky Callisto, for Artemis' aim did not miss.

Amorous adventures did not please Artemis, who was no less famous for her chastity than for her hunting. Alpheius, a river god, fell in love with her and pursued her to Elis. But Artemis and her companion nymphs smeared their faces with mud, so that they could not be told apart, and drove Alpheius away with mockery. And when Actaeon caught her unawares while she was bathing, he paid a terrible price for the privilege of seeing her naked. She turned him into a stag and set his own dogs on him so that they tore him to pieces.

Though Artemis was the scourge of lesser beings, and men and beasts had no chance of escape when she took aim, her passionless nature made her no favourite on Olympus. Once, when the gods were quarrelling above the plains of Troy, Hera turned on Artemis and beat her like a naughty kitchen-maid. She snatched the quiver and bow from the great huntress and thumped her about the head with them until Artemis burst into tears and fled snivelling to her father Zeus—who had to listen to yet another catalogue of complaint against his short-tempered consort.

But in the world below Olympus, the divine huntress was too threatening and important to disregard. First, she gave useful benefits to mankind, not only as the goddess who controlled the fortune of the hunt, but also as a goddess of childbirth and one of the divine patrons of medicine, with particular success in curing snake bites. All the animals of the world came under her care. It was her first task to conserve the beasts of the wild, and only her second to destroy them, in the hunt for food or when they became too dangerous. Those who did not respect her animal kingdom felt the fire of her anger.

## Aphrodite, goddess of love

Love, as all mankind knows, is a source of trouble. And Aphrodite, goddess of love, had a well-earned reputation on Olympus as a trouble-maker. Love was the sport of the gods, which they followed ardently, and Aphrodite had the magic girdle which could make any one of them irresistible.

The poets, when they told us her story, found something wild and alien in Aphrodite. Her beginnings were savage, mirroring the tales of other passionate goddesses who reigned in the east. She was born of the foam that gathered around the severed genitals of Uranus, when his son Cronus flung them into the sea. She rose naked from the waves, and floating on a scallop shell, came first to the little island of Cythera, and then to Paphos, in Cyprus, where grass and flowers sprang up beneath her feet. The Seasons, the daughters of Themis, met her and clothed her, and from the first she was accompanied by Eros and Desire. This Eros was not, as later degenerate times have shown him, a chubby, winged son of Aphrodite but an ancient deity well known in Boeotia and Mysia, and his power to stir up hearts was equal to that of Aphrodite.

Aphrodite's only interest was love. She was mistress of the arts and mysteries, of all the ways of enticement and seduction, and in her person she exemplified feminine beauty and allure. Though unsurpassed in beauty, she was jealous of competition. When Myrrha, daughter of King Cinyras of Cyprus, dared to compare herself with Aphrodite, the goddess inflicted her with an incestuous love. Her father was ready to kill her, but Myrrha fled and prayed to the gods who turned her into a myrrh, or balsam, tree. When her child was due to be born, the bark of the tree split and revealed the lovely boy Adonis.

Aphrodite, ashamed of her mischief, claimed the boy, and put him in a chest which she gave to Persephone to keep safely in the Underworld. After a time, when Persephone opened the chest and saw how handsome Adonis was, she refused to return the youth to Aphrodite but kept him as a favourite in her own palace. Both goddesses appealed to Zeus but the Father of the Gods, not liking this unseemly wrangling between the goddesses, sent the case to the Muse Calliope to judge. Deciding that Aphrodite had a claim on his birth and Persephone on his upbringing, Calliope divided Adonis' time between the goddesses and also gave the youth a third of the year to himself, to live as he pleased.

But Aphrodite cheated on the bargain. When her turn came to care for Adonis, she used her wiles and her magic girdle to make Adonis infatuated with her. Persephone took her new grievance to Ares for advice. The god of war despised the beautiful youth, who devoted himself to the soft hours of the night rather than to the harsh day on the battlefield. So Ares dealt with the matter in his typical brutish way. He changed himself into a boar of particular ferocity and attacked Adonis as he hunted on Mount Lebanon. Severely gored, Adonis slowly bled to death. As his blood stained the ground, red anemones sprang up; and roses, until then all white, also turned red, coloured by Aphrodite's blood, as, running to her dying lover's side, she scratched her arm on the thorns of a rose-bush.

To Aphrodite, love governed all. Under her influence mortals suffered and died, denying family, country and responsibility for her sake. Anchises of Troy was one human who fell under her spell. Greatly desiring this handsome mortal, Aphrodite prepared herself with all the wiles she knew, so that even the animals were infatuated as she passed; then she went to Anchises as he lay asleep among his flocks on Mount Ida. At dawn, after a night of love, the goddess revealed her identity, promised that the child to be born of their meeting would one day be famous, and ordered Anchises to keep their affair a secret. But Anchises, when he had been drinking, boasted of his conquest and angry Zeus hurled down a thunderbolt. Some say the bolt killed Anchises, but others that Aphrodite managed to divert the blow,

though the shock waves from the thunderbolt left Anchises weak and crippled for ever after.

Not all suffered for love, for Aphrodite had it in her power to be kind to those who felt the pangs of her influence. Pygmalion, a sculptor of Cyprus, was granted a very great favour by the goddess. He made an ivory statue which he modelled on Aphrodite herself. When he saw the results of his efforts, the beauty of the face and the grace of the figure, he fell in love with his own handiwork. He prayed to Aphrodite to grant him a wife who was as lovely as his own statue. The goddess, touched by his request and not without conceit, went one better than his prayer and made the statue itself come alive. The living statue was named Galatea, and lucky Pygmalion was now able to marry a woman who resembled, as far as was humanly possible, the great goddess of love herself. Their son was Paphos, bearing the same name as Aphrodite's most holy shrine on the island of Cyprus.

The power of love, which Aphrodite used to disrupt the affairs of mankind, also had its effect on Olympus. Zeus gave Aphrodite in marriage to Hephaestus, the god who worked the heavenly forge. But lame Hephaestus was clumsy and uncouth and Aphrodite was soon inflaming divine hearts elsewhere. The story of her affair with brawny Ares, god of war, has already been told, with its ludicrous consequence, when the lovers were caught in Hephaestus' net. But such are the compulsions of the flesh, love does not feel shame for long. Aphrodite returned to Cyprus and renewed her virginity in the sea that had given her birth. Then she was ready once more for the games of love.

Though her activities were often mischievous or hurtful, Aphrodite could not be ignored, neither on Olympus nor in the world of man. Her influence was too widespread. Both men and women worshipped her as the great goddess of love, drawn to her ways of passion and desire. Even Zeus himself fell continually under her enormous powers as one beauty after another—mortal, nymph or goddess—held him captive on the field of love.

## The goddesses

Among the oldest representations of the human form that have survived from prehistoric times are little figures carved in stone or moulded in baked clay, recognizable as women by their exaggerated sexual characteristics. They are found where traces have survived of the earliest farming villages.

In primitive agricultural communities the germination of the buried seed and the subsequent harvest of edible grain must have at first seemed a precarious annual miracle. The reproduction of crops on earth was seen as a process similar to that of the reproduction of humans in the womb and it was celebrated as such in art and ritual, to ensure the continuation of the miracle.

Thus the earth was worshipped as a Mother Goddess: Demeter means Earth Mother—the giver of fertility. Before the Greek-speaking peoples found their way to Greece, bringing their sky-god Zeus, the most important deities of the Mediterranean peoples seem to have been fertility goddesses. Male deities seem to have been merely their consorts, necessary for the goddesses to fulfil their role in reproduction.

The story of Demeter and Iasius making love in a thrice-ploughed field seems to confirm this view of gods and goddesses. In many primitive agricultural communities all over the world anthropologists have recorded rituals in which the fertilization of the earth by the sky (rain) is symbolized by a 'sacred marriage' enacted in the fields. The story of Demeter and Iasius tells of just such an occasion.

It is possible that all, or most, of the Olympian goddesses were originally fertility goddesses. Hera is, among other things, goddess of marriage. Artemis, though herself a virgin, is, among other things, the protectress of women in childbirth as well as the protectress of animals; and Aphrodite, as goddess of love, is naturally associated with procreation. Hestia and Athene are exceptions: neither has any interest in sex or fertility.

Hestia was a goddess of great antiquity—the oldest child of Cronus and Rhea, and deserving the deepest respect. She personified all that the family home (in Greek the *oikos*) meant to its members. These were,

basically, the husband and father (master of the *oikos*), his (usually much younger) wife, their young children, the household servant (a slave), perhaps elderly dependants and any animals the family possessed. All these Hestia protected and she received a daily tribute paid by the master of the *oikos* at the altar beside the hearth.

Athene, from time immemorial, had been worshipped at a shrine on the Athenian Acropolis. Athens had once been a Mycenaean city, and the Acropolis the site of the palace of the Mycenaean kings, so, it is inferred, Athene must have been their protecting goddess and her shrine their private chapel.

Regardless, however, of what the goddesses had been in the dim and distant past, by the time of Homer they had acquired sharply differentiated personalities and many interests that had nothing to do with reproduction. In Homer's male-dominated world they had shrunk in importance by comparison with the male gods, especially Zeus 'Father of gods and men'. Yet in this, too, Athene is the exception. Unlike Hera, Aphrodite and Artemis she is never in the Homeric poems treated with disrespect by either gods or men, though she frequently interferes in war and politics—as Demeter and Hestia never do. Apart from her skill in weaving —a task for women—she is wholly unfeminine in her personality and her interests.

## Aphrodite, Eros and Dione

Eros ('love') is always associated with Aphrodite, although he came into existence before her, as one of the first heavenly creatures. In some later myths he becomes her son, a charming winged boy who makes mortals fall in love by shooting arrows of desire into their hearts.

The philosopher Plato claimed that there were two Aphrodites: firstly the daughter of Uranus ('heaven') who was the goddess of pure 'heavenly' love, and secondly the daughter of Zeus and Dione who was the goddess of sexual passion. This is why people talk of 'platonic love' when they mean love without sexual passion.

# THE MYSTERIOUS ONES

## The mysteries of creation

The poets have told us of the descent of the gods and how they made the world. But some have not been content with that, for they see in the wonder of the universe a mystery which mankind can barely comprehend.

To many, this is a strange way of thinking. We try to account for the world so that plain men will recognize it. But some singers and visionaries have come among us from far away, from the wild, northern lands of Thrace and Phrygia, and they have urged us to look beyond what seems ordinary and reasonable into the mystical nature of things.

About the creation of the world, the visionary followers of Orpheus related this story. The goddess Night, in the form of a gigantic black bird, emerged out of Chaos and Darkness. The Wind fertilized her and she brought forth a silver egg, in which was Eros. This god was also called Phanes, or 'the Revealed One'. Eros-Phanes, with four horns and four eyes and great golden wings, contained within him both sexes, being a woman before and a man behind. Sometimes he roared like

### The Greeks and religion

Religion is essentially something that is experienced. The experience can, in rare circumstances, be communicated to an outsider by poetry or even by prose, but in attempts to describe, explain or analyse it the essence always seems to evaporate.

Writers on Greek religion often begin with five negative statements. There were for the Greeks no sacred books, no dogmas, no priesthood, no sermons and no orthodoxy, and therefore no religious persecution. Some of the things we know about the Greeks seem to contradict these statements but they do not really do so. For example, if there were no sacred books, why are the epics of Homer sometimes called 'The Bible of the Greeks'? Certainly, most Greeks owed to the epics their ideas of the gods and goddesses and, in part at least, they were known by heart by educated Greeks and quoted to provide examples of how one should, or should not, behave. Nevertheless there was nothing sacrosanct about the *Iliad* and *Odyssey*.

If there was no priesthood, who were the men and women called by Greek words which are translated 'priest' and 'priestess'? In fact, these were for the most part amateurs exercising an honorific ceremonial function which might be elective and temporary (like our Lord Mayors and Lady Mayoresses). Greek priests and priestesses were not 'Reverend', 'Right Reverend' or 'Venerable' in the literal sense of these titles.

Disbelief in the gods was rare, shocking and, if expressed, might even result in prosecution. Very few people, however, were punished for atheism and when they were there were usually political undertones to the prosecution. On the other hand to make fun of the gods was perfectly acceptable.

One positive statement that all scholars make about Greek religion is that for the Greeks religion was all-pervasive. It was ever present in the home with the altars of Hestia and Zeus which received their daily tribute, and in the figure of Hermes outside the doors. When the Greek stepped outside his home he found shrines, altars and temples to the gods and goddesses all around him, all the more conspicuous because all domestic architecture, even the town houses of the rich, was plain and modest—not to say, in many cases, primitive—and did not compete for attention with the statues and temple sculpture that celebrated the gods and a lion, or bellowed like a bull, or hissed like a snake. He was dazzling to look on, so much so that his mother Night named him 'the Firstborn Shining One'. They lived hidden in a cave, for none but Night could face the full radiance of the Shining One.

Then Eros-Phanes created the earth and the sky and the moon, and he set the sun to watch over them. Rhea, the Great Mother, sat in front of the cave and beat a bronze drum, to announce to all outside the presence of the oracle of the goddess within. Night showed herself in three ways, being also Order and Justice, but Eros-Phanes held the sceptre of government. This, he passed on to Uranus after whom came Cronus and then Zeus, as we also believed. The followers of Orpheus, however, saw another age. The reign of Zeus, they said, was destined to pass away, and the reign of the god Dionysus would come into being.

their deeds. Festivals of the gods involved ceremonial processions on foot or horseback, torch races, solemn presentations at the temples, festivals of song, drama or athletics and in all of these religion and civic pride were intermingled. Nor was it only civic pomp that celebrated the gods. Village ceremonies continued to be honoured, since it was in the countryside that the Greek religion had its roots. Ploughing and sowing and harvesting and other activities of the agricultural year were all hallowed in the ceremonials along with rituals for cleansing houses and farmsteads of evil influences.

It is difficult today to have a sympathetic understanding of Greek religion because the triumph of Christianity in the fourth century AD created a sharp break in the religious thinking and feeling of the western world. The old religion of the Greeks and Romans lingered on for many years and those who continued to practise it were nicknamed 'pagans', probably because the Latin word *paganus* meant 'a civilian' and pagans had not enlisted as soldiers of Christ in the battle against Satan.

# Dionysus, god of wine

All are agreed that Dionysus was the son of Zeus and the youngest of the gods. But the dervishes and mystics who followed Dionysus out of his native Thrace had many wonders to relate about this god, and since they spoke with the tongues of ecstasy and vision, mankind can only grope towards the truth.

Many say that Dionysus was also called Zagreus, a child whom Persephone conceived in guilt when her father Zeus came to her as a serpent. Hera, learning of the birth, angrily stirred up the ancient Titans to destroy the child. They beguiled the baby with the toys of infancy, a ball, a mirror, golden apples, a bull-roarer and pretty pieces of wool; then they set upon him with their faces disguised by chalk. Zagreus tried to evade them by changing his form, from child to lion to horse to bull, but he could not escape. The Titans tore him apart and devoured him. Only his heart was saved and taken by Athene to his father. Zeus swallowed the heart and then destroyed the Titans with his mighty thunderbolts. From their bodies, mankind was born, a race that took from the dead Titans some of their wickedness and some of their divinity. But Zeus, having within him the heart of Zagreus, formed the child once more, this time in the womb of Semele.

However, most followers of the god had a different account. They say that Zeus lay directly with the mortal Semele, who then had to suffer Hera's jealous anger. Appearing as a wise old woman, Hera cunningly pretended to pity Semele, saying that her love-making had been incomplete, since Zeus had withheld from her his full divinity. Foolish Semele petitioned her lover to show himself as a god and Zeus appeared to her in all his splendour. Semele's mortal frailty could not withstand his divine glory: the lightning that blazed from him consumed her utterly, but seared Dionysus, in her womb, into divine immortality. Zeus snatched the unborn child from the ashes and placed him inside his own thigh until the time of birth arrived.

Lacking a mother, Dionysus was nursed by his aunt Ino. But Hera's vengeance was not yet complete. She sent madness to Ino and her husband, causing him to kill their son and her to jump from a cliff, destroying both herself and her second child. To escape the wrath of Hera, Dionysus was taken to Mount Nysa where the nymphs of the mountain cared for him in rural seclusion. His only childhood companions were women, except for Silenus, the dissolute and effeminate old satyr who was his tutor. Either by his own genius or guided by the tastes of Silenus, young Dionysus discovered how to ferment grapes into wine. The god's powerful liquid was well received by his followers. Wreathed with ivy and laurel, Dionysus led them on the riotous path of ecstasy.

Followers flocked to his cause. His first worshippers were the gentle nymphs of Nysa who adored him, hiding their faces modestly behind their winnowing-fans. Then, when the secret of wine was revealed, a wild army of votaries collected around him, mortals and half-beasts, satyrs, fauns, Centaurs, and the raging women known as Maenads. They had snakes around their arms, and announced the god's arrival with bull-roarers, carrying the thyrsus, a staff wound with ivy and tipped with a pine-cone, which was both a symbol and a weapon. Dancing and drinking, they grew possessed and had the strength of madness, tearing animals and even humans apart with bare hands, quite indifferent to the pain of fire or wounds. And leading them, also possessed, was their lord Dionysus; for in a final act of revenge Hera had put a divine frenzy on him and driven him out into the world without peace or rest.

Dionysus travelled to many distant lands, his rabble at his heels, propagating the vine as he went. From far away, strange whispers were told of savage conduct and miraculous deeds. It was said that he defeated the Titans. That he fought the Amazons in Libya and flayed a king alive in Syria.

That he rode a tiger in Babylon and herded elephants in India. When his period of frenzy was over he turned back from India. Some say that it was Rhea, consort of Cronus, who released him from his madness and initiated him into the rituals and mysteries of the Great Mother.

The long journey back to his own lands began, but opposition and troubles met him on the way. In Thrace, King Lycurgus made a murderous attack on the satyrs and Maenads who travelled with him. Dionysus himself leaped into the sea with fear and took refuge for a time with Thetis beneath the waves. Lycurgus was punished with madness, the usual punishment for the opponents of the god. Believing that he was destroying the pernicious vine, the king killed his own son, hacking his limbs like stubborn branches. The earth, in horror, became barren and would not bear crops again until the boy's cruel death was avenged. At the command of Dionysus, the people condemned their king to be pulled apart by wild horses.

On another journey, Dionysus was captured by Tyrrhenian pirates. Seeing such a handsome youth, the pirates planned to sell him as a slave, though the experienced pilot warned that the magnificent stranger 'might be a god'. Soon his fear was confirmed. A vine began to wind about the mast, wine flooded the decks and seeped through the planking, and Dionysus, changed into a lion, chased the pirates into the sea, transforming them there from men to dolphins. Ever after, dolphins have remembered this lesson inflicted on their former selves and are friendly to all seafarers.

Wherever Dionysus landed, the wild revels of his followers were met by suspicion and fear. In Thebes, his mother Semele's own city, he was almost arrested by King Pentheus as a charlatan and vagabond. But Pentheus was unable to subdue the raging Maenads, and followed them to Mount Cithaeron, to spy out their rituals. Disguised as a woman, he hid in the branches of a tree but a sudden movement of the leaves revealed his hiding place; the frenzied women pulled him from his hiding place and tore him apart, with his own mother leading the demented attack.

In Attica, Dionysus was at first made welcome. The vines were planted and tended and the grapes grew round and sweet. But when the first vintage came and wine was made for the first time, the people took the unaccustomed drink and thought they had been poisoned. In rage they killed the man who had welcomed Dionysus and his dangerous vines into the kingdom.

Those who opposed or resisted Dionysus were swiftly brought low, afflicted with madness, driven to acts of terrible destruction. But even when Dionysus was kind there was danger in his kindness. King Midas, he who grew ass's ears for insulting Apollo, met the ragged army of Dionysus as it straggled towards India. He set them on the right road and thus won the favour of Dionysus, who offered the king anything he wished in return. Immediately, Midas replied: 'Grant that everything I touch be turned to gold.' The wish was granted. Wherever Midas went, he left a trail of gold behind. Rocks, trees, flowers, the doors of his palace, household objects, even his clothes, all became gold at a touch. Food and drink changed to gold as he lifted it to his lips and Midas was likely to starve to death.

In panic, Midas begged Dionysus to release him from the fatal gift and was instructed to bathe his body in the River Pactolus. The waters took away the golden touch, but the sands of the river bed are speckled with gold to this day.

Slowly, after much resistance, the cult of Dionysus was established in the lands of mankind, though some still held out against him. In Orchomenos, the daughters of Minyas refused to join the worship, preferring to continue quietly with their weaving. Dionysus himself took the form of a maiden to advise them to take part; and, when they would not, he filled their room with wild music, caused weird phantasms to flit across their looms, and made vines grow into the weaving. The three maddened women cast lots to choose a sacrifice and, in their frenzy, tore the son of Leucippe, the eldest, to pieces as an offering to the angry god, then ran to hide their shame. This sacrifice did not appease Dionysus, who drove the women from mankind, transformed into a bat, an owl and a crow.

At last Dionysus, with his triumphal following of devotees and dervishes, conquered the fears of all the world. Through the god and through his holy gift of wine, his followers loosed themselves from human inhibitions. Possessed by divine frenzy, in an ecstasy from drink and dancing and the blood of sacrifice, they became one with the god, looking into realms beyond the eyes of ordinary men.

Then Dionysus claimed his reward. First, he released his mother, Semele, from the Underworld where Zeus' lightning had sent her long before. Next, he ascended to Olympus, to claim his rightful place among the gods. Zeus made him welcome. The Father of the Gods took Dionysus by the hand and led him to a place of glory, by the right side of the celestial throne.

## Dionysus and a new religion

One usually thinks of religion as a cohesive element in social life, inducing feelings of loyalty and belonging. But of course there are also manifestations of religious feeling which are socially disruptive, dissolving normal constraints and subversive of authority. This type of religious manifestation naturally attracts members of a community who are undervalued, frustrated or oppressed. In Greece this was particularly the case with women. For them the arrival of an exotic god whose rites called for orgiastic behaviour on the mountain tops was an opportunity to release themselves from the housebound lives of demure respectability imposed on them by their menfolk. The myths about Dionysus could be considered fanciful accounts of an episode of Greek history when a new religion of the disruptive sort led to the clashes between its devotees and representatives of masculine authority. By the fifth century B C, Dionysus was celebrated at a range of different festivals, including a biennial ceremony of Bacchic dances on Mount Parnassus above Delphi, a tamed and institutionalized version of some wilder form of worship.

What makes such a pallid interpretation of the myths inappropriate is the survival of Euripides' tragedy *The Bacchae*. In this tragedy Dionysus is the embodiment, both seductive and terrifying, of powerful psychic forces which are released by music and dancing. The dancing becomes wilder and wilder and takes the individual Bacchanals (also known as Maenads) far beyond the control of themselves or of anyone else and makes them capable of acts of supernatural strength, endurance and destructiveness.

The wild dances of the Maenads are the most spectacular and disturbing element in the worship of Dionysus, but his worship had much to offer to men as well as women. As the god who had brought the vine to Greece it was natural that he should be the patron god of Athenian countrymen, for whom the vine and the olive were staple crops. There were many Athenian festivals dedicated to him, in particular those of tragedy and comedy. Among his several roles was that of promoting fertility. He could transform himself into a bull or a goat—both creatures of great reproductive power—and not surprisingly the comedies and the satyr plays performed in his honour were bawdy. His role as wine-god was most prominent in another festival dedicated to him—the Anthesteria. This took place in February/March and celebrated the first opening of the jars in which the previous year's vintage had been stored. The wine was drunk in accordance with special rituals at public banquets, in silence, everyone beginning to drink simultaneously at the sound of a trumpet. The festival lasted three days. The first two were devoted to drinking and seem to have been fairly riotous. The final day was concerned with the sinister presence of the ghosts of the dead and included offerings to Hermes, one of whose duties was to escort the recently dead down to the Underworld. This mingling of the celebration of earthly joys with rituals designed to keep the forces of evil at bay is one of many paradoxes involved in the worship of a god who concealed terrifying powers beneath an appearance of effeminate hedonism.

## The mysteries of Eleusis

The followers of Dionysus brought riot and violence into the worship of the gods. Few were safe when the holy rage was upon them, and Death kept close to their heels. But there were certain singers of Orpheus who also celebrated a gentler mystery in which the goddess Demeter permitted the initiates a different understanding of the inner meaning of the world.

This secret knowledge, which men called the Mysteries, began in that painful time when Demeter searched from land to land for her daughter Persephone, whom Hades had snatched so rudely down to the Underworld. In her wanderings, say the disciples of Orpheus, Demeter came to Eleusis and, in the guise of an old woman, rested disconsolately by the Well of Maidenhood. When the daughters of the king found her there, they comforted her and led her home. After a drink of mint and barley-water, Demeter was taken to Queen Metaneira, who took her as nurse to her infant son.

But now, as you have heard before, a tragedy happened. As Demeter tempered the child in the fire to burn away mortality, Metaneira came upon the fiery scene and screamed in alarm. Demeter threw the child on the ground, assumed her own divine form and reproached the queen, ordering her to build a temple at Eleusis in the name of Demeter.

Before the temple could be built, Demeter took up her search once more. When she returned to Eleusis her task was done. One joyful day Persephone, released from the infernal kingdom by the command of Zeus, travelled upward in Hades' golden chariot and fell into the arms of her waiting mother. At once, Demeter freed the land from the blight which her sorrow had cast over it. Then she summoned the members of the royal house of Eleusis and made them the priests of her temple, instructing them in the secret rites of the Mysteries which would lead the initiated to a blessed afterlife.

Among those instructed, Demeter looked most kindly on Triptolemus, a son of the king, for he had helped her in the search for Persephone. The people of Eleusis claim that she gave him the first corn, and taught him to yoke oxen to sow it. He tilled the plains of Eleusis and in due time reaped the first golden harvest and he built the first threshing-floor. Then Demeter gave him a chariot drawn by winged dragons, and he flew through the world carrying seed and teaching men to use it. When he inherited the throne of Eleusis, he devoted himself to the service of the goddess, dedicating the pig to her in sacrifices, and establishing the forms of worship to be used in the Mysteries.

On the fifteenth day of the month of Boedromion, just before the autumn sowing, the festival of the Mysteries began. The followers of the goddess (the Mystai) gathered, taking oaths of purity and secrecy, and undergoing a ritual purification. Late at night, they went in procession towards Eleusis, dancing and waving torches and singing hymns. They stopped at wayside shrines and sacrificed to the image of the infant Iacchus, the mysterious cult-god who, they believed, was Dionysus in a different form. Next, they meditated on the suffering of Demeter, preparing their hearts to feel her anguish, roaming the seashore and the wild places as she had done in her search for Persephone. At last they felt at one with her, sharing her understanding of the nature of things, recognizing through her pain the eternal suffering of mankind. They gave thanks to the goddess and feasted together, passing among them certain sacred objects. The last act of the festival was so holy none dared speak of it. All we can know is that the Mystai went to the Hall of Initiation from which came the sounds and strange music of some sacred drama, unfit for profane eyes. When the Mystai emerged they were filled with the grace of Demeter, fully prepared for that final moment when the grim ferryman would take them across the Styx, down to the shadowy realm of Queen Persephone.

Because the infant god Iacchus was Dionysus in another form, the Mystai of Demeter and the ecstatics of Dionysus were sharers in the one great secret. This was how it happened. On the way to Eleusis, Demeter, in disguise, had met a woman called Baubo by the roadside. Pitying the careworn traveller, Baubo offered her a drink of barley-water, but Demeter was preoccupied with her search and set it aside untouched. Then Baubo lifted her dress and revealed her womb, in which Demeter, with immortal's sight, clearly saw the child Iacchus. The baby was laughing and seemed so happy that the goddess laughed too. Her burden of grief was eased and she took the drink. Because he had consoled Demeter, for ever after Iacchus had his place in the worship of the goddess at Eleusis.

Nothing more was known about Iacchus, for he hid himself from all except those initiated into the Mysteries. But one miracle was accounted to him in later years. When the armies of Xerxes the Persian were advancing over the wasted plains of Athens before the battle of Salamis, certain men of Athens and Sparta who were with the Persians saw a vast cloud of dust, such as 30,000 soldiers might make, towering over Eleusis. As the cloud moved over the empty, ravaged land towards the naval camp at Salamis, there issued from it the deep sounds of the hymn which was sung to Iacchus in the practice of the Mysteries. Then men knew that the Persians were doomed.

## The secret society

Eleusis was a little town situated in a particularly fertile area of Attica. The area had been cultivated and the site inhabited at least since Mycenaean times and a shrine of great antiquity was located there. In this shrine a goddess—probably a pre-Greek earth mother—had long been worshipped. Not surprisingly she was identified with the Olympian goddess Demeter. Over the remains of this shrine in the sixth century BC there was built a hall. Later in the century it was improved and extended by the tyrant Peisistratus, and it was again extended twice in the fifth century. This hall was large and rectangular and had stepped seating suitable for a large audience. Within the hall was an enclosed inner shrine. Three priests controlled the building and its precinct, and everything that went on there. They were always chosen from two very ancient Eleusinian families. In the hall took place the preliminaries to the initiation ceremonies known as the 'Eleusinian Mysteries'. The final ceremonies took place in the inner shrine. These were secret and the penalty for disclosing them was death. Scholars differ in their guesses as to what did go on in the inner shrine, but it is known that certain 'secrets' about life after death were revealed and that candidates for initiation had to

recite certain formulas. Whether they were also required to undertake any special rules of conduct is a matter of dispute. The 'mysteries' were open to anyone (including slaves and foreigners) who knew enough Greek to recite the formula and had not committed murder. Whatever the 'secrets' were, it is clear that they promised to the initiates the protection of Demeter in the life after death.

Demeter was, naturally, the most important divinity in the initiation ceremonies. Also important was Iacchus, an ambiguous god, represented in art as a child and regarded sometimes as the son of Demeter, sometimes of Persephone, sometimes of Dionysus, and sometimes as Dionysus himself.

The 'mysteries' were celebrated twice a year, once (the less important ceremony) in the month called by the Athenians Anthesterion after the festival Anthesteria (literally 'flower-festival') which included wine-drinking ceremonies and was in honour of Dionysus, and again (with a grand procession from Athens and Eleusis) in the month of Boedromion (very roughly translatable as 'running to help' and so-called in memory of help in battle given by the god Apollo to Theseus against the Amazons and on other occasions). Anthesterion corresponds roughly with our March, and Boedromion with September.

# Orpheus and Eurydice

Who was the mortal Orpheus whose disciples dared to challenge the order of Olympus, spreading among mankind the secret rites that belonged to Demeter and Dionysus?

Orpheus, all agree, was the greatest poet and musician who ever lived. He was born in Thrace, son of the king of the land and of the Muse Calliope. His mother and her sister Muses taught him his art; and Apollo, in recognition of his genius, gave him a lyre. Soon Orpheus made such astounding progress that he performed as well as the god himself. When he played, the savage beasts drew near, and even rocks and trees moved from their places to find the source of the music. And to these talents he added magic and secret wisdom, for he was a devoted follower of Dionysus, the god of his native Thrace.

When he grew to manhood Orpheus wooed and married the dryad Eurydice. But their happiness did not last long. One day, in the vale of Tempe, Eurydice was waylaid and assaulted. She escaped, but in her headlong flight she stumbled on a snake, whose fatal bite stole her life and plunged her ghost down to the kingdom of Hades.

Made reckless with grief, Orpheus decided to fetch her back from the infernal region. Having nothing but his lyre to help him, he set out to charm his way with music through the black realm of the Underworld. As he played, grim Charon let him pass the ferry over the Styx, and the three heads of the dog Cerberus nodded to sleep, lulled by the sweet sounds. In the Fields of Asphodel, Orpheus softly plucked his lyre before the Judges of the Dead and they did not detain him. Then he passed down to the black halls of Tartarus, where even the implacable heart of King Hades melted with music. Hades agreed to release Eurydice, but on one condition. Orpheus must not look back at her until they reached the safety of the upper world.

They set out through the dark realm, Orpheus walking ahead and guiding the steps of his beloved with gentle sounds from his lyre. Every so often he stopped and listened for the sound of her footfall and then passed on. Patiently, Eurydice followed the sound of the music. All through the steep and winding way from the dark Underworld, Orpheus kept his eyes fixed steadfastly on the blackness before him. All went well until Orpheus was about to burst out into the sunlit air. He stopped and listened intently. He strained his ears for the slightest sound, but not even a rustle or a tiny squeak of a sandal reached him from the soft step of Eurydice. In panic he swung round, fearing that she was lost—and caught for a fleeting moment the despairing look on Eurydice's face. Then she was truly lost to him forever, plucked by Hades from Orpheus' outstretching arms and thrust back into the vast, dark House of the Dead.

Without Eurydice, Orpheus was inconsolable. Some say he became a priest of Apollo in the temple on Mount Pangaeum. Certainly, he no

longer wanted anything to do with women, and for this reason the Maenads and the women who followed Dionysus grew to hate him. One day, when the ecstatic fury came upon them, they laid hold of Orpheus and tore him to pieces.

When the Maenads had finished their terrible work, they flung his head into the River Hebrus.

Still singing, it floated down to the sea. Then, as it drifted to its final resting place on the island of Lesbos, the music and the burden of the song it sang wafted over the passing lands, teaching with the incomparable art of the master the story of poor Orpheus and how he reconciled his sorrow in the mystery of the gods.

## The religion of Orpheus

Orphism was a minority religion for those who were unhappy with life as it is lived on earth. Conscious of the wickedness and injustice that flourished unchecked and the transient nature of earthly pleasures, they put their faith in an afterlife, rejecting the robust Homeric acceptance of the joys and tragedies of human existence.

This faith required an alternative creation myth to the generally accepted one. So the story of the primordial egg and Phanes was evolved. The most important elements of the myth were the killing and eating of Zagreus-Dionysus by the Titans, the blasting of the Titans by the thunderbolts of Zeus and the creation of mankind from the ashes of their bodies. The significance of this story is that the human soul contains a divine element (from Dionysus) and an evil element (from the Titans). Because of the initial wickedness of our Titan ancestors our souls are compelled to endure life on earth, not just once but for successive reincarnations until they have, by pure living, purged themselves of sin. These reincarnations can take place not only in human form, but also as animals or even certain plants.

This doctrine of the transmigration of souls was taught by Pythagoras the great pioneer of mathematics. In the sixth century B C he founded a brotherhood of disciples which ruled the Greek city of Croton in South Italy for a generation, until they were massacred in a revolution.

Orpheus was a legendary figure, imagined as the first ever poet and singer, the son of Calliope, the muse of epic poetry. Since no poems by him were in existence it was possible to attribute to him newly concocted poetry, teaching new doctrines about the soul and its destiny.

The Orphics and Pythagoreans were vegetarians (not surprisingly, since an animal might contain the soul of a kinsman) and 'purified' themselves by various rites of washing and incantations. By strict rules of conduct they mortified their bodies, which they regarded as the tombs of their souls (*soma—sema*, body equals tomb, was an Orphic motto).

According to Orphic doctrine, the soul could, after several reincarnations, be set free to everlasting happiness; but only through strict obedience to Orphic rules of abstinence and strict attention to Orphic rituals. Those who did not adopt the Orphic way of life had to endure many more reincarnations than those who did, while the incurably sinful were condemned to everlasting punishment.

This doctrine of reincarnation has similarities to Buddhism (whose founder lived about the same time as Pythagoras) and both beliefs are probably derived from the same Hindu source.

Orphic ideas influenced many Greeks who did not become followers of the Orphic way of life—in particular the philosopher Plato. Nonetheless Orphism was a religion only for the few. The poor and oppressed of fifth century Greece, who might have been attracted to the promise of better things after death, were not attracted to a lifetime of strict vegetarianism and mortification of the flesh. The Eleusinian mysteries offered a much more appealing passport to special treatment in the afterlife. To be initiated into these, you needed no commitment to a life of discipline. As long as you had not committed murder, you needed only to purify yourself, rather expensively, just before the initiation.

# THE NATURE OF THE WORLD

## Prometheus and Pandora

It is wise to speak of the past with caution, for memory becomes muddled and our fathers' fathers dissolve into worlds of mystery, but it is the opinion of many that mankind co-existed with the gods of Olympus from the beginning. For in the end both families, human and divine, are the children of Mother Earth.

Wherever our forefathers lived, lonely and apart from all others, they gave thanks to Earth who nourished them, and traced their line back to her beneficence. Some say mankind sprang from the blood of the wounded Uranus, when his son Cronus mutilated and deposed him. The far-flung drops fertilized Earth and brought forth not only giants, nymphs and furies, but also the first men. Each man, rising up far apart and solitary, at first knew nothing of any other. So for the Athenians, Cecrops was the first man, who came out of the ground of Attica, mortal but not wholly human, being still part snake. The people of Boeotia honoured their ancestor Alalcomeneus as the first man, born like a fish in the waters of Lake Copais. The Arcadians pointed to their own earth-born Pelasgus, while the Thebans dated their existence from certain dragon's teeth which were sown at Thebes and later germinated into men. The Thebans began with many people, but Aeacus, first man of Aegina, had a country with no other human inhabitants until Zeus took pity on him and turned the ants of the island into citizens. The men of Argos, however, claim that the first man was their ancestor Phoroneus who sprang, not directly from Mother Earth, but from the union of the river god Inachus and a nymph. They say that when Prometheus brought fire down from the gods, Phoroneus taught man how to use it, and under his guidance the people of Argos advanced most quickly from the simple condition of beasts.

Prometheus the Titan, son of Iapetus and Clymene, was so important in the destiny of mankind, that it was natural men should honour him, even calling him the creator of mankind. These people say that he took clay from Panopea, in Boeotia, and shaped it into the features of a man. Then Athene helped him to bring it to life. To this day, petrified remnants of the clay can be seen in Panopea where Prometheus discarded them.

Iapetus, brother of Cronus, had four children: Atlas, Menoetius, wise Prometheus, the 'Forethinker' and candid, unsuspecting Epimetheus, the 'Afterthinker'. Prometheus was subtle and wise beyond most of the Titans and the gods and knew the secret fate of both. From Themis, the Titan, he knew the greatest secret of all: the mother who would bear a son, destined to overthrow the reign of Zeus. In the contest between the Titans and the younger gods for the power of heaven, Prometheus was at first on the side of Zeus, for he foresaw the ultimate victory of the Olympian gods. And Zeus was glad to use his cunning and his advice. But Prometheus, with his secret knowledge, was dangerous to Zeus. Moreover, Zeus had taken a hatred towards men, whom he regarded as upstarts and potential rivals, while Prometheus was their champion. If he was, indeed, their creator, that would be only natural. To Prometheus, Zeus' distrust and hatred of mankind seemed absurd, a petty jealousy in one so full of power. But Prometheus was apprehensive and with good reason, for Zeus plotted to kill off the pernicious race of man entirely.

About this time, a contention arose between men and gods as to how the ritual sacrifice should be apportioned. The disputants met to decide the matter, with Prometheus as the final arbiter. Sympathetic to the humans, Prometheus dismembered the sacrificial ox, stuffed the good meat into its stomach and wrapped the bones and hide temptingly in the glistening fat. Then he invited Zeus to choose the gods' portion. Some say Zeus was deceived by his greed, others that he only pretended to be deceived in order to test his opponents. Whether through greed or cunning, the result became the same: Zeus snatched the attractive fatty part that lay before him and discovered too late that it hid only a handful of bones. The choice was made and ever after this, when men made sacrifices, the bones were given to the gods while the men ate the best of the meat at the sacrificial feast.

In his anger, Zeus now withheld fire from the world, so that men would eat raw meat only. But Prometheus went secretly to heaven and stole fire from the gods (some say from Hephaestus' forge, and some say from the fiery chariot of the sun) and carried the gift to earth hidden in a hollow stalk of fennel.

More angry than ever, Zeus planned a truly spiteful revenge against mankind. Until this time, men had existed on earth without women. Now Zeus ordered Hephaestus, the divine smith, to make a clay figure modelled on the Olympian goddesses. When this was done, Athene breathed life into it, Aphrodite gave it grace and beauty, Hermes endowed it with cunning and trickery, the Graces and the Seasons adorned it in the most bewitching way. This, the first woman, was called Pandora, or 'All Gifts', because all the gods had bestowed gifts upon her. Hermes led her down to earth and presented her to Epimetheus, for Zeus knew that though the wily Prometheus would suspect a trick, Epimetheus would welcome the gift as what it seemed to be. Prometheus had warned his brother to have nothing to do with any gift from the gods, but Epimetheus, who was without guile, was captivated by Pandora's beauty.

Formerly, men had lived without sorrow and without effort, existing like happy beasts, as content with life as horses in a rich summer pasture. But Pandora, who was as foolish as she was beautiful, had with her a large jar in which were imprisoned all forms of suffering, evil and disease. The jar was sealed and she was warned by Epimetheus never to look inside; but curiosity was stronger than caution. She broke the seal, and all the wrongs and afflictions which have since become the lot of mankind flew out into the world. Only false Hope was left in the jar, the delusion which persuades mankind still to struggle on against trial and pain and injustice.

In this way, Zeus was avenged on man. But there was still a reckoning to come with man's protector, Prometheus, he who had dared to oppose his will against the Father of the Gods. At once, Zeus sent Hephaestus out to capture the Titan, taking with him two mighty helpers, Cratus and Bia, whose names mean Strength and Force. They bound Prometheus, dragged him to the Caucasus mountains, far from the lands of men, and chained him to a rocky peak. Each day, an eagle tore at his liver; each night, the liver grew again. And there, through the ages, he endured, an immortal who wished to die, sustained only by the secret which Themis had told him and which Zeus still could not learn.

For unknown ages, the two great powers, Olympian and Titan, remained like this, in angry and painful tension. Then the Fates at last decreed that the hero Heracles should travel through the Caucasus, and pass by the peak to which Prometheus stood bound. Heracles shot the torturing eagle and released Prometheus from his agony. In gratitude, the Titan at last revealed to Zeus his greatest secret: that it was Thetis, daughter of Nereus, whose son was destined to overthrow the reign of Zeus—but only if the father of that son should be a god. Zeus, who had planned to take the Nereid to his bed, took notice of the warning, for he knew that Prometheus was among the wisest of all beings. He married Thetis to the mortal Peleus, so that their human son, Achilles, though powerful indeed among men, would be no danger to the divine order of Olympus.

## Gods, men and sacrifices

Before Darwin thought out the theory of evolution the questions 'where did human beings first come from, and why?' could only be answered by a myth. Mesopotamian myths had an answer. The gods created human beings because they wanted slaves to keep them provided with food. Hesiod, whose poetry tells the Greek creation story, explains just why and how women were created, but about the origins of men he is contradictory and confused. One modern scholar has suggested a reason. The Greeks knew of the Mesopotamian myths but neither Hesiod nor any other Greek was willing to believe that human beings were the slaves of the gods. So the subject remained vague, although many cities liked to tell myths about how their own citizens originated.

The Prometheus myths tackle the very difficult subject of the relations between gods and human beings. If men were not created to be the slaves of the gods, what then was the relationship between them? Greeks believed that men and gods came closest together at the ritual of a sacrifice. Greek sacrifices took several forms; the only necessary item was an altar. This could be a large and elaborately carved slab of stone or a simple table of turf. Sacrificial offerings could be bloodless, consisting of wine, milk, honey, oil or fruit — and the ceremony could be a private affair or a large public function. Private sacrifices could be a father with his family giving thanks for a meal, or a few friends together wanting the favour of the gods for some commercial enterprise; public sacrifices were a function of the state.

Public state sacrifices were very expensive, involving the killing of many animals (cattle, sheep or pigs were the most common, though to certain special gods other animals such as dogs, asses or horses were sacrificed). After the animals had been killed according to a strict ritual they would be cut up and the fat and thigh bones would be put on the altar to burn; the meaty parts would be divided up and distributed for all those present to feast on. Such sacrifices (and the occasional domestic sacrifices of small animals) were the only occasions when Greeks would eat meat; normally their diet was vegetarian. A public sacrifice, and the feast that followed it, was a solemn and important occasion — the Greek equivalent, in some respects, of a Christian communion service.

There was, however, one aspect of the sacrifice that seems to have bothered the Greeks. If it was a shared feast why did the god, in whose honour it was held, receive only the fat and the bones? The answer given by logic would have been that the god's share was a token gift and the fat burning on the altar conveyed the aroma to the gods better than the meat would have done — if only because fat burns better. The answer given by the myth of Prometheus was that it was by their own choice that the gods had the fat and bones, but it was an unintentional choice and Zeus had been tricked into making it. Men had then been made to pay for Prometheus' trickery by the coming of Pandora and the contents of her jar. So the score was even and men could enjoy their sacrificial feasts without any feelings of guilt.

This neat tit-for-tat story is very much more like a folktale than a religious myth. Nevertheless the whole myth, despite its folktale appearance, may be trying to say something serious about the kinship between god and man. The Greeks seem to have believed that men once met and ate with the gods on terms of intimacy. Things then went wrong because Prometheus, who, as a Titan, was neither god nor man but somewhere between, tried to outsmart Zeus on behalf of men.

In the story of the Garden of Eden it is the serpent who comes between Man and God by tempting Eve to disobedience, knowing that she will tempt Adam. The fruit of the forbidden tree brings knowledge and with it disaster. Despite many differences there seems to be just enough resemblance to suggest that the Prometheus story may be concerned with some of the same problems as Genesis, problems which are far removed from the plots and fantasies of a folktale. It is clear from the confusions of Hesiod's narrative that he had difficulties with his story. He wanted to believe that Zeus was a great, wise and just god, but if Prometheus could deceive Zeus about the sacrifice, then Zeus could not be so very wise. The character of Prometheus, too, is confusing. In Genesis there is nothing good to be said about the serpent who caused the Fall of Man. By contrast Prometheus, though it was he who caused Zeus to be angry with men, was usually regarded as a benefactor of mankind.

# The five ages

In the time of Cronus was the Golden Age of men. Then they lived as carefree as the gods, neither working nor feeling sorrow, and the good things of the earth fell as a natural harvest into their hands. They did not grow old, but after an appointed time slipped quietly away, as if into profound sleep. Their spirits went to heaven, and there, by the will of Zeus, became the guardians of those left behind.

This mortal race served its time and after it came the Silver Age, in all respects debased from that which went before. The men of this time, though divinely created, clung to their mothers' skirts for a hundred years, then fretted out short lives in foolishness and sin. They did not worship the gods nor did they sacrifice on the holy altars. Zeus swept them away so that they were hidden in the earth and became the spirits of the Underworld.

Then Zeus created, out of the nymphs of the ash tree, the third race of the Bronze Age. The people of this age ate meat not bread. They were strong, violent and warlike creatures, wearing bronze armour, and slew each other in interminable quarrels. A black death carried them all down to the cold house of Hades.

Then Zeus tried yet again. This time he made the nobler, more just men of the Heroic Age, the demi-gods who fought before the seven gates of Thebes, and in the land of Cadmus, and over the sea on the sun-baked plains of Troy. They fought so well, they drove their race to extinction, but Zeus reserved for them a life after death. By the stream of Oceanus, in the Isles of the Blessed at the edge of the world, their spirits lived on happily under the kind rule of Cronus.

Then came the present age, which is the Age of Iron. This is the time of evil, when there is neither reverence nor justice nor respect for age. Oaths mean nothing, the cruel man rends the innocent, neighbour oppresses neighbour, plagues and war banish peace and all contentment. Man is sunk forever in his iniquity, and the poets are left to lament his fate.

## The races of Men

Should we believe in progress? Or is it the case that we, the human race, have been becoming more greedy, more cruel and more destructive from generation to generation? Probably most people, when they think about it, believe that, though there are some bad side-effects, scientific and medical discoveries have made our lives happier than those of our ancestors and will continue to do so.

For a short time the Greeks, too, were optimistic about the improvement of life on earth. In the fifth century B C after they had defeated the Persian invasion and freed the cities of Ionia they enjoyed a period of confidence in themselves and their future. The inventions of history and geography, together with philosophy and scientific speculation seemed to promise boundless intellectual progress. Advances were being made, too, in medicine, mathematics, astronomy and town planning.

Disillusion came at the end of the fifth century. There was the great plague and the long and bitter war between Athens and Sparta and the even more bitter civil wars that broke out in many of the cities involved in that war. From then on very many — perhaps most — Greeks believed that for mortal men things are bad and will either stay bad or get worse. There were some Greeks who believed that life on earth moved through an endless succession of cycles in which age succeeded age, each age worse than the last, until finally the cycle came to its end and the Golden Age returned. Then the whole process would begin again.

There were also Greeks who regarded the advances in knowledge and skill and the practical achievements of human beings as not an advance but a decline. The best thing men or women could do was to train themselves to live contentedly, 'according to Nature', wanting nothing beyond the bare necessities of life. The Greeks who preached these beliefs called themselves Cynic philosophers and practised what they preached, living like the begging friars of the Middle Ages, or Buddhist monks in the Far East, or like the hippies of the 1960s.

# Deucalion, Pyrrha and the flood

At the end of the Age of Bronze, Zeus saw the wickedness of mankind, and he determined to exterminate them. He opened the sluices of heaven and let the rains flood upon the earth. The waters rose in every land and only a few escaped the flood. Megarus, founder of Megara, was guided to safety by the cry of the cranes flying overhead. And Dardanus, of the royal house of Troy, fled from Samothrace in a boat of skins, drifting over to the oriental shore as the mighty waters, pushing the land apart, opened the passage between Europe and Asia. But the race of man, except for the favoured few, was swept away.

In this catastrophe, mankind was saved once more by the intervention of Prometheus and his family. Still chained to the Caucasian rock, Prometheus foresaw the coming of the flood, and by some means—it is said a passing bird carried the message—sent word to his son Deucalion, bidding him build and stock an ark, and then go aboard with his wife Pyrrha, daughter of Epimetheus and Pandora. Then the gates of heaven opened, and the wind blew, and the waters rose above every city and every household in the lands of mankind. For nine days and nights the ark floated, tossed by storms, battered by waves which swept the decks and draped the mast with trailing weeds. On the tenth day the flood began to subside and the boat came to rest on the summit of Mount Parnassus.

Deucalion and Pyrrha disembarked on the bleak mountain-top, still draped with the things of the sea, and immediately made sacrifice to Zeus, humbly petitioning that the race of men should be established once more. The anger of the Father of the Gods was assuaged by the timely sacrifice. He sent Hermes to say that the prayer was granted, and by the order of the gods Deucalion threw stones over his shoulder, which became men, while the stones that Pyrrha threw turned into women. Ever since then, in the language of our peoples, the word for 'stone' and the word 'people' are almost the same and from the same root.

After the flood, an equilibrium was struck between gods and men. Each had an appointed task and place. Mankind, mortal, lowly in power and subject to grief, was not wholly separate from the gods, being possessors, perhaps, of an everlasting flame. The light of heaven still shone on men and made them sharers in some part of the divine. Or was that the delusive Hope that alone remained within Pandora's jar?

## The Flood myth

Everyone has heard of Noah's Ark: Deucalion and Pyrrha are less familiar. Yet Noah and Deucalion are almost certainly the heroes of different versions of the same story, which came originally from Babylonia.

The ancient cities of Babylonia owed all their prosperity, their very existence even, to the rivers Tigris and Euphrates. When the snows in the distant mountains melt each spring these rivers rise and the lands of Mesopotamia would be flooded if they were not protected by engineering works, as they have been for thousands of years. There is a very ancient Mesopotamian myth about a catastrophic flood sent by the gods to destroy all mankind with the exception of one man and his family. Evidence has been uncovered by archaeologists to show that large areas of the very early Mesopotamian cities were washed away by flood water. In Greece, however, there are no great rivers and the only floods are the result of sudden heavy storms turning relatively small streams into raging torrents. These subside as quickly as they rise. The same is true of the lands of the Bible. Disastrous floods which would provide an historical basis for a flood myth are therefore unlikely and scholars therefore conclude that the Greek and Hebrew myths of the flood are simply versions of the Mesopotamian myth.

Like the story of the creation of men and women, a flood myth, however, occurs in many widely separated societies, from the Australian aborigines to the Indians of South America, and seems to be a fundamental mythological theme.

# The world of the Greeks

After Earth and Heaven emerged out of Chaos, they gave form to all the places of the living and the dead.

High above the world of human beings, frowning Olympus was the home of the gods. There Zeus kept state, studying the fates of men, and in the palaces the gods held discourse, feasting on nectar and ambrosia, foods fit for immortals only, while the divine ichor flowed in their veins instead of blood. The days of the Olympians were eternally bright. Storms never touched them; neither rain nor cloud nor rough winds disturbed the serenity of their home.

Below the realm of the gods were the lands of mankind. Best known to men were those territories loosely ranged around Olympus, from where the gods looked down and favoured those who worshipped them. But the inhabited lands faded into mystery towards the far shores that bordered the encircling stream of Oceanus.

At the western edge, Atlas, son of the Titan Iapetus, held the sky on his shoulders. Atlas had fought for the Titans against the Olympian gods, and Zeus, in punishment, had condemned him to carry the sky forever on his shoulders. Close to his feet lay the Garden of the Hesperides, daughters of Evening who kept watch on the Golden Apples which Mother Earth had given to Hera as a wedding present. They sang as they watched, and their safety was assured by Ladon, a dragon in shape and ferocity but speaking the language of men.

In the west, also, lived Hemera and Nyx, the Day and the Night. These two were never at home at the same time, for as the one returned from daily labour, the other set out with the cover of darkness. Close by Night were her children Hypnos and Thanatos, or Sleep and Death. The first was a gentle friend to man; but the other clutched the unfortunate in an iron grip from which there was no escape.

By the eastern shore of Oceanus was the land of Aea, where Jason went in search of the golden fleece. And in the east, too, was the palace of the sun god Helius, which he left each morning for his journey across the sky. Far to the south, and to the east, the dark-skinned Ethiopians lived. Still further away, by the hot southern shore of Oceanus, were the Pygmies, a race of little people who waged a deadly war with their enemies, the cranes. But in the north were the cold lands, the dank realm of the Cimmerians where the sun never broke through the swirl of the mists, and, next to them, the territories of the Hyperboreans, a land sacred to Apollo.

Tartarus lay beneath the earth, as far below the ground as the sky was above it. And all the space between Tartarus and the earth was the dark kingdom of Hades.

## Greek geography

Accurate maps and descriptions of the earth's surface depend in the first place on travel and exploration, measurement and an understanding of the shape of our planet. The seamen of Minoan Crete (2000 – 1400 B C) had explored the coasts of the western Mediterranean for the purposes of trade: this is known because Minoan pottery has been dug up in many places where it could only have been transported by Minoans. The Mycenaeans followed in their wake, some scholars say more for piracy than trade. After the collapse of the Mycenaean civilization and during the Dark Ages, life in Greece and the Aegean islands was too much of a struggle for survival for anyone to undertake naval enterprises. Instead the Phoenicians from Tyre and Sidon (in what is now the Lebanon) became the pioneering explorers of the western Mediterranean. Nevertheless in Greece and Ionia memories of past voyages survived in folktales, myths and legends. Some of these were incorporated into the *Odyssey*, Homer's story of the wanderings of Odysseus on his return from the siege of Troy.

In our century a few amateur scholars have sailed round the Mediterranean and the Black Sea, attempting to retrace Odysseus' voyage, but they have not convinced many people that there is much real-life geography in the story of a voyage which included encounters with one-eyed giants, lotus-eaters, sirens, the God of the Winds and a sorceress with a beautiful voice.

About the time that Homer was composing the *Odyssey*, Greeks began again to travel and explore. Unlike the great navigators and explorers of the Age of Discovery, Greek sailors lacked the compass for navigation, ship's rigging and steering-gear suitable for sailing close to the wind, mechanical clocks for measuring time and gunpowder for driving off hostile natives. The unknown perils of the rocky coasts, treacherous currents and sudden storms of the Mediterranean added to the possibilities of a fierce reception from the inhabitants of the shoreline, made voyages of exploration in the Mediterranean and Black Sea daunting enough to require brave and resourceful sailors, even without the giants and sorceresses.

On the other hand it was not necessary to be an

The world as Herodotus described it in the fifth century BC. Herodotus thought the source of the Nile was somewhere south of the Sahara, where the River Niger flows.
He realized that there were many lands to the east and north of Greece but no Greek had visited them so nothing was known about them.

intrepid sailor to visit Egypt and other parts of the Persian Empire—though no doubt it required much energy and enterprise. Travellers such as Hecataeus and, later, the fifth-century BC historian Herodotus, probably contributed as much to Greek knowledge of the earth's surface by their travels and shrewd questioning as the sailors and traders did, especially as they recorded what they had learned, whereas the traders usually liked to keep their knowledge a secret from rival traders.

From the Persians, travellers could learn about the Persian Gulf, the Caspian Sea and India as far as the River Indus. From the Egyptians they could learn about the Red Sea coast and the country on either side of the upper Nile. The actual source of the Nile was a tantalizing mystery to the Egyptians. Herodotus tells us (not all scholars believe him) that he travelled as far as Elephantine, near the first cataract of the Nile but for knowledge of the land further south he was dependent on what he could learn by enquiry. From the Greeks who had founded a colony at Cyrene in Libya he learned about the Sahara and heard a story about a Libyan expedition which succeeded in crossing it. The members of the expedition (five dare-devil young tribesmen) were captured—so he was told—by pygmies and taken through swamps to a city near which was a great river, flowing from west to east. In this river they saw crocodiles. Modern scholars think the river must have been the Niger but Herodotus guessed that it was the Nile. This fitted his picture of the world as consisting of two symmetrical halves. Everything south of the Mediterranean was, according to Herodotus' theory, the mirror image of everything north of it. Thus the Nile was the southern equivalent of the Danube and bisected Africa (which he called Libya) just as the Danube bisected Europe. Though Herodotus' world picture was radically wrong, it was an improvement on that of Hecataeus. Hecataeus' world picture still had a river named Ocean encircling the earth: Herodotus says, 'I do not know any River "Ocean", but suppose that Homer, or some other poet of long ago, invented the name and put it into his poetry.' A century after the time of Herodotus, in the fourth century BC, Alexander the Great, the Greek king of Macedon, set out to conquer the Persian Empire. He took with him on his campaigns geographers and surveyors who recorded a mass of useful observations. These were studied in the centres of learning set up after Alexander's death in Alexandria, Rhodes and Pergamum. By the end of the first century AD Greek geographers had realized that the earth was a globe with two poles and an equator. They marked their maps of the world—as far as they knew it—with lines of latitude and longitude and five zones (two frigid, two temperate and one torrid). One Greek geographer (Eratosthenes) made a fairly accurate calculation of the circumference of the earth. The last of the great Greek geographers (Ptolemy), however, underestimated the circumference. As he did not know of the existence of America he thought it would be possible to sail across the Atlantic to China. His geographical writings survived the fall of the Roman Empire and the subsequent Dark Ages and were read by the explorers of the 'Age of Discovery'. That is how Christopher Columbus came to set off westwards for China, and so accidentally discovered America.

# Gods of the natural world

We have told how after the battle with the Titans, the gods of Olympus confirmed their victory by apportioning the world between the sons of Cronus. Zeus, the Thunderer, was lord of the heavens, Poseidon had charge of the seas, and Hades ruled the Underworld. The surface of the earth was common ground where each god and goddess exercised some power and influence.

But long before the triumph of Zeus, Mother Earth had ensured the survival of the universe by bringing forth the spirits and the deities who governed all the manifestations of nature. The lords of Olympus were overseers of great work which Earth, in her primal wisdom, had set in motion for the good of all the world.

The first deity of the sun was Hyperion the Titan. But when his wife Thea produced a child called Helius, this radiant youth took over the duties of his father and drove the chariot of the sun. Each morning, Helius set out from his palace far to the east, near the land of Colchis. He harnessed his immortal four-horse team and drove the blazing chariot across the sky to the stream of Oceanus in the west. There, he unhitched his horses and pastured them in the fields of the Isle of the Blessed, while be bathed himself in the waters and rested. Then, in the darkness, the encircling flow of Oceanus carried the god and his team in a great bowl back to the eastern palace, ready for the new day.

Helius had little business on earth, for his realm was the sky, from where his all-seeing eyes encompassed the world. From his high vantage point, he saw and took note, and carried news to the other gods. When territory on earth was first distributed among the gods, sky-borne Helius was overlooked; the little island of Rhodes was given to him as an afterthought when it appeared above the waves and also Sicily, whose rocks and earth were flung into the sea when the giants fought the gods. Besides these islands, Helius also owned herds of three hundred and fifty cattle and three hundred and fifty sheep, which he kept pastured far to the west, on the island of Thrinacie.

By Poseidon's daughter, Helius had seven sons who ruled on Rhodes. In honour of the sun god, their descendants constructed the famous Colossus, a figure seventy cubits tall, a wonder of our ancient world.

By Clymene, daughter of Minyas, Helius had a son called Phaethon. This youth, who grew up with Clymene, at last set out to find his father. After long wanderings he came to the sun's palace, far to the east, and Helius was so happy to see his long-lost child that he invited Phaethon to choose any gift he wanted. Phaethon asked to be allowed to drive the chariot of the sun for one day. Helius was horrified, for he knew the difficulty of the task, but he had given his word and could not now withdraw his promise. Next morning the youth harnessed the spirited horses to the radiant chariot and set off. But the task was beyond him. As the four horses plunged and wheeled, the chariot of the sun raced behind. In their mad career, sometimes the horses pulled the sun so high that men almost froze. And sometimes they dived so low in the sky that the flames of the sun shrivelled the earth. The lands of Libya were scorched into a desert and the skin of the Ethiopians turned black with the burning heat. Some say that the drought became so widespread that, to halt its progress, Zeus made the rivers of the world overflow their banks and so brought the great flood which overwhelmed mankind.

As the earth smouldered and froze under Phaethon's erratic course, Ge called out to Zeus in alarm, and he struck Phaethon from the chariot with a thunderbolt. Helius resumed the reins and Phaethon fell dead into the River Eridanus far below. There his mourning sisters, weeping on the banks, were turned into the trees from which the tears of amber always flow, in memory of Phaethon's golden youth.

Helius was not the only child of Hyperion and Thea. In particular, he had two sisters called Selene and Eos, whose names mean Moon and Dawn. Selene borrowed her dim light from her brother Helius and, like him, she drove a chariot through the sky, though hers was drawn by two, not four, horses. Like Helius also, Selene had few dealings with mankind, but once she fell in love with the mortal Endymion, said to be the most handsome of men. She visited him where he slept in a cave and gently kissed his eyes. Endymion was thrown into a perpetual sleep in which he never aged; the bloom of youth remained always on his fair cheeks as he slept on for all eternity.

But rosy-fingered Eos, unlike brother Sun and sister Moon, was very much concerned with the world of men. She was a great beauty and a keen participant in the rites of love, cursed, some say, by Aphrodite in a fit of jealousy. Selene's love was destined never to grow old but Eos' consort, Tithonus, met a different fate. Wishing to save him from the common lot of men, she begged great Zeus to grant him immortality but forgot to ask for agelessness as well. Tithonus lived on but grew older and smaller and so shrunken that Eos hid him in a chest, in the end able only to listen to his voice, which alone had remained strong and youthful.

Before Poseidon became lord of all the world's waters, Mother Earth gave birth to Pontus, the primeval deity of the sea, and he brought forth Nereus, the wise Old Man of the Sea whom men called 'the teller of truth'. Nereus could change his shape at will and gave prophecies to all who asked, for he was a kindly sea god with no destructive urge towards shipwreck or storm. By Doris, daughter of Oceanus, Nereus fathered the fifty Nereids, all of them gentle mermaids and sea nymphs.

But Phorcys and Ceto, also children of Pontus, were progenitors to many fearful children. Two monsters sprang from them: Ladon, the dragon who guarded the Golden Apples of the Hesperides, and Echidna, a serpent-woman who ate raw flesh. Echidna coupled with the terrible giant Typhon, and their progeny were even more frightening to look on. Next, Phorcys and Ceto brought forth the three Graeae, hag-like and grey-haired from birth, who had but one eye and

one tooth between them; and then the hideous
Gorgons, sisters whose names were Stheno, Euryale
and Medusa. These were the strange offspring from
the sea, within whose hidden depths more
grotesque and monstrous forms may lurk unknown
to man.

The rivers, waters more friendly to mankind,
were all the children of the Titans, Oceanus and
Tethys, and so too were the three thousand ocean
nymphs, the Oceanides, who acted as helpers and
guardians to the youth of mankind.

As for the winds, the giant Typhon brought forth
the treacherous and useless damp airs which crept
over low ground as mist or blanketed the seas with
fog. But the breezes which served mankind were
the gift of the gods, being the children of the Titan
Astraeus and Eos, the Dawn. Their names were
Boreas, Eurus, Notus and Zephyrus, being
respectively the winds of the North, East, South
and West. Though often beneficial, these winds
were boisterous and unruly. Sometimes they
assaulted maidens; or they would change to
stallions and mount mares in the field. Zeus feared
the rough, unpredictable strength of the winds,
and when they were not blowing he confined them
to the floating island of Lipara where Aeolus was
their guardian. Seated within the cave of the
winds, Aeolus kept a prudent eye on his mercurial
charges. When the gods called for them, he
released them carefully, by unstopping a hole in
the island's cliffs.

Earth had other dangerous beings, the worst of
whom were the giants. Ge brought forth these
children from the blood of Uranus and, when the
Titans had been defeated, incited the vast and
terrible creatures to attack the gods of Olympus.
The warfare was fierce and savage, pitting the great
strength of the giants against the immortal power
of the Olympians. Mountains and hills were
uprooted and flung about like stones, crashing into
the sea to form new islands around the coasts.
With difficulty, the Olympians struggled to victory.
Many giants were imprisoned, thrust beneath the
mountains, disturbing them for ever after with
their volcanic rumbles of anger and distress.

# Pan, god of the countryside

On high Olympus, many gods and goddesses
shared the work of looking after the natural world.
But Pan, ancient nature god, old enough to be
called the foster-brother of great Zeus, was not
quite respectable and had no place on Olympus.
He lived in the wilds of his native Arcadia, the
goat-legged familiar of beasts and herds and flocks
and mountain-nymphs, a merry and irreverent god
of all the countryside.

Like many obscure deities whose old line
descended from Mother Earth, Pan was of
uncertain birth. Most acknowledged him to be the
son of Hermes by Dryope, though Cronus and
Rhea, and many others, have been called his
parents. He was so ugly at birth, with his goat's
legs, horns and beard, it is said his mother ran
away from him. But he was a fertile, talented god,
easy-going on the whole, liking nothing better than
a nap in the heat of the day. In the woods and the
summer pastures of the hillside he calmed flocks
and herds with accomplished music, especially
when he played on the pipes named after him.

His figure was goatish, and so too was his lust.
He deceived Selene, the Moon, by covering his
smelly rusticity with fine white fleeces and
tempting her to ride on him. He pursued several
gentle nymphs, who fled from his brutish manners
with unhappy results. Syrinx, a Hamadryad or
wood nymph, escaped him by sinking below a bed
of reeds. Pan cut the hollow reeds and turned them
into the first pan-pipe. Pitys also fled from him,
and only found refuge by changing into a pine tree.
Poor Echo was a third unlucky victim. When Pan
could not catch her, he turned some local
shepherds mad and they tore at Echo until only her
voice survived. In matters of love, Pan's appetite
seemed insatiable and it was best for every maiden
in the woods and fields to keep a careful watch
against him.

Such a vulgar, low god, not wanted on
Olympus, was not much respected by mankind
either. But he could be bad-tempered and mean,

especially if his nap was disturbed. Then he afflicted men with a sudden, wild, blind fear which drove them mad, and which now goes by the name of 'panic'. But he could also help men. Before the battle of Marathon, when Pheidippides was running to Sparta for help, Pan fell in with him by Mount Parthenion and told him not to despair, for Pan was a friend of Athens and would help the city again. Pan did not lie and, after their famous victory, the grateful Athenians built a shrine to Pan under the brow of the Acropolis.

Who can be certain of the ultimate fate of the gods, though they are called immortal? Pan alone is known to have died. In the time of Tiberius, when a ship was going from Greece to Italy, a mighty voice summoned the Egyptian helmsman. 'Thamuz,' it cried, 'when you come to Palodes, tell them great Pan is dead.' Thamuz delivered his message and everywhere there were lamentations and grief, for the death of a god is no small matter.

## Pan and Arcadia

In Attica the countryman's god was Dionysus, the god of the vine. Pan was the countryman's god in western Greece in the land-locked, mountainous and thickly forested land of Arcadia, a land especially suitable for shepherds and goatherds. The Arcadians, in the eyes of the rest of Greece, were a people whom history and civilization had passed by. The Dorian invaders who brought about the downfall of the Mycenaean world in the twelfth century BC left them alone but settled all around them, isolating them from access to the sea and from other states. In the course of time Arcadia acquired the reputation of being a backward area of strange rites and strange happenings; there were rumours of child sacrifice and werewolves. The Arcadian god Pan, however, acquired worshippers outside Arcadia, especially after the Battle of Marathon when the Athenians routed an invading Persian army, killing 6400 Persians for the loss of 192 of their own men. It was such a dramatic and unexpected victory that the gods, it was felt, must have been fighting for the Athenians. The story of Pan's encounter with the runner Pheidippides, his promise of help and the Athenian shrine established after the victory must all have contributed to the spread of his worship.

When Christianity came to the ancient world the early Christian teachers did not deny that the pagan gods existed but said that they were evil demons. When mediaeval artists wanted to depict the devil they made him in the likeness of Pan, with horns and cloven hooves and shaggy goat-like legs. They added a long forked tail which Pan did not have.

## The idealized countryside

With the exception of the artisans and market traders of Athens and Corinth — large cities by Greek standards — virtually all Greeks worked in the country. Agricultural workers do not usually idealize the countryside. Hesiod describes his farm as being near Mount Helicon, in the 'miserable' village of Ascra which, he said, is 'bad in winter, intolerable in summer and never good'. Homer, Euripides and Sophocles, all town dwellers, described more idealized scenes. Homer describes scenes of merrymaking in the vineyards as the grapes are being harvested; Euripides told of Hippolytus' joy in the beauty of the woods and meadows, while Sophocles in his last play wrote with deep affection of the beauties of the groves at Colonus where the nightingale sings and the crocus and narcissus flower. Nevertheless in the classical period of Greek literature no great interest is shown in the beauties of the countryside. It seems as if most educated Greeks were rather like Socrates who confessed (according to Plato) that he never went outside Athens because he was a lover of knowledge and it was city-dwellers who taught him knowledge, not the trees or the countryside.

The greatest Greek poet of the countryside was Theocritus, who based his poems on the herdsmen's traditional singing and piping contests. Subtly interwoven in his songs are evocations of the countryside of Sicily (where he grew up) or of the Aegean island of Cos, where he lived for a time.

# The Underworld

Everything below the earth, down to the deepest depth of Tartarus, belonged to the kingdom of Hades. When mortals died, they received the rites of burial—at the very least a covering of dust—for without these the ghost would find no rest. The coin called *obol*, the price for the ferryman, was placed beneath the tongue. Then Hermes, the messenger of the gods, took the departed by the hand to the border of the Underworld.

Some say the downward way had many entrances, but who knows the truth? Men do not return to tell their tale. The broad path to the afterlife began by the western stream of Oceanus, in the land of the Cimmerians where the sun never shone. At the confluence of the rivers that separated the living from the dead stood the White Rock, and a grove of willows and poplars, sacred to Persephone, marked the point of departure.

Five rivers delineated the world of the dead: Styx, Acheron, Phlegethon, Cocytus and Lethe—the rivers of Hate, of Woe, of Fire, of Wailing, and of Forgetfulness. Styx, in whose name the gods swore their inviolable oaths, lay at the boundary which the shades of the mortals must cross, and there Charon, the grim and tattered ferryman, grabbed his coin. Cerberus, the three-headed dog, guarded the far bank, to make sure none returned; those few favoured heroes who did retrace their steps bribed the guard-dog with a honey-cake. Passing the river, the dead came to the Plains of Asphodel, in which they dwelt if they were neither good nor bad, leading a shadowy existence without hope or despair, without pain or pleasure, compared to which a life among the dregs in the meanest hovel on earth was preferable.

Hades ruled the Underworld with Queen Persephone by his side, but neither judged the dead. That duty was shared by three stern figures. Aeacus judged the shades from Europe, Rhadamanthys judged those from Asia, and Minos took the most difficult cases. The majority of the dead, shades of no distinction, stayed on the Plains of Asphodel. The wicked went down to Tartarus. But a few great mortals, in whose veins ran the blood of the gods, or who had made their mark by heroic acts, went to the Isles of the Blessed, Elysium, a land governed by Cronus and set apart from the dead and the damned by the stream of Oceanus. Hunting and sporting and making music, the fortunate few existed in eternal happiness, under the balsam trees in meadows that blazed with golden flowers.

But for the sinful and the wicked, the horrors of Tartarus awaited, and the Erinyes, or Furies, with their terrible, implacable faces, pursued without mercy those who had offended, especially those who sinned against the ties of family or kinship. The Erinyes, children of Ge, were born at the beginning of things and were not subject to the Olympian gods. Their name must not be mentioned, but in appeasement they were called the Eumenides, 'the Kindly Ones'. Their wrath could not be turned aside. They were ready to hound their victim to the grave. When kinship was violated, even in the cause of justice, the command of a god meant nothing to the Furies.

As far below the ground as an anvil would take nine days and nights to fall lay Tartarus. An iron palisade with monstrous gates surrounded the place of darkness, pain and punishment, and the hundred-handed giants stood watch outside. This was the place allotted by the stern judges to those who 'dared great wickedness and accomplished what they dared'.

# The great offenders

The greatest infamy belonged to those who set their hands against the gods. Some crimes were simple in their enormity, like those of Tityus and Ixion. The giant Tityus was bound fast in Tartarus while two vultures tore perpetually at his liver, for he had tried to rape Leto, the mother of Apollo and Artemis. The offence of Ixion was even more appalling. He made a plan to seduce Hera, consort of Zeus himself. The Father of the Gods read his intention and formed the clouds into the figure of Hera. Ixion, drunk and lustful, tried to ravish the cloudy image. Zeus caught him in the act, bound him to a fiery wheel, and hurled him down to Tartarus where Ixion revolved forever.

These stark crimes deserved, and received, instant retribution. But Tantalus and Sisyphus were punished for a more complicated web of offence.

Tantalus was born the most fortunate of men. Growing up in wealth and power, he also had the favour of the gods, so much so that he was granted the hospitality of Olympus. He sat at the divine banquet, eating the divine food, and he began to think himself the equal of the gods. He invited the Olympians to come and feast with him at his palace in Sipylus, and, out of some devilry or foolish arrogance, he decided to put them to a test. As a special dish, he had his own son Pelops butchered and cooked and served to the gods. Of course, the Heavenly Ones, when they came to eat, were not deceived by this abominable dish: only Demeter, sadly preoccupied by the loss of her daughter Persephone, ate a piece from the shoulder of Pelops.

Horrified by what Tantalus had done, Zeus commanded that Pelops be restored. Hermes gathered the butchered pieces and Zeus made the youth whole; except for the damaged shoulder which he replaced with ivory. Then, when the goddess Rhea had breathed life into the body, the gods turned their anger on Tantalus. They recalled other grounds for complaint. Had not Tantalus also betrayed their confidence, revealing their conversation on Olympus and taking the holy nectar and ambrosia from their feasts? Had he not hidden the golden dog which had watched over the infant Zeus in Crete? And had he not denied the theft until Hermes had discovered it on Mount Sipylus?

For all these offences, Zeus condemned Tantalus to everlasting punishment. Some say he was suspended in air, touching neither heaven nor earth, with the sun blazing over him like a fiery stone. But most agree that he was fixed in a lake in Tartarus, overhung with fruit trees. The waters lapped up to his chin and the ripe fruit swayed by his forehead. Agonized by hunger and thirst, Tantalus could neither eat nor drink; for when he reached towards a fruit, the wind whipped it away, and when he bent to drink, the water receded to the black mud.

Tantalus' sins were breath-taking, but Sisyphus of Corinth showed, if possible, even more contempt for the gods. Sisyphus had a well-deserved reputation for intelligence and cunning, so when the river god Asopus discovered that Zeus, in one of his amorous forays, had abducted his daughter Aegina, he asked Sisyphus where the girl was to be found. A bargain was struck. Asopus provided Corinth with a spring of pure water, and Sisyphus disclosed where Aegina was hiding. Asopus, an ancient deity with no great respect for the Olympians, set out after Zeus in a hot temper, and the Father of the Gods only managed to escape by changing himself into a stone.

Now Zeus raged against Sisyphus for revealing his secret and ordered Hades to arrest him and drag him to the Underworld in chains. Again, Sisyphus used his wiles and tricked Hades into testing the chains on himself. Swiftly, he snapped the locks shut and held the god of death a prisoner.

While Hades was absent from his realm, none could gain entry to the afterlife and Death himself was cheated of his victims. In consternation, Ares, slayer of men, rushed to help his companion, Death, and released Hades from his bonds; and the sad pilgrimage of the shades began again.

But Sisyphus was still at liberty and had another trick to fool the gods. When Hades came once more to fetch his ghost away, Sisyphus whispered to his wife to leave his mortal body unburied. The judges of the Underworld would not accept a shade unfortified by the rites of burial, so Sisyphus was rejected and sent back across the Styx to earth. Some say that Sisyphus outwitted the gods and died peacefully in his old age. But then at last Hermes took him sternly by the hand and led him to the fate ordained for him.

Down in Tartarus, Zeus had arranged his punishment. A gigantic rock was set at the foot of a steep hill and it was Sisyphus' task to push it to the summit. With groaning limbs and shoulders rubbed raw by the stone, Sisyphus set his exhausted strength against the rock and step by heavy step he laboured up the slope. But each time, as he came within a handsbreadth of the top, the rock slipped from his grasp and rolled back to the bottom. Back it came, again and again, for all eternity.

The gods shall not be mocked. Mankind is warned by the example of these miscreants, those who in pride and foolishness contend against the will of heaven. Inevitably, the punishments of Tartarus await them.

## Life after death

The one constant feature about Greek beliefs concerning the fate of the dead is the importance of a proper funeral, whether by burial or cremation. Apart from this, opinions varied from the dim ghostly existence in Hades of the Homeric heroes to the belief in a blessed release from the prison of the body entertained by the followers of Orphism. The philosopher Plato (about 428—347 BC) expressed his own beliefs by inventing a myth. The myth told of the warrior Er who appeared to have been killed in battle, but came to life again when lying on his funeral pyre. He recounted what had happened to him on his death. He had found himself, he said, journeying to a mysterious place where there were two openings in the earth. On arrival, the souls of the dead were directed by judges either downwards (the bad) or upwards (the good), but Er was told that it was his destiny to report back to the world of the living everything he saw and heard. What he saw and heard (to give a brief account which does no justice to the fascination of Plato's quite elaborate myth) was as follows:

As the souls of the recently dead departed by the two openings, other souls emerged from two identical openings, coming back from a journey of a thousand years. Those who came from below were dusty and travel-worn, those from above clean and bright. As they met they exchanged accounts of their experiences. For every wrong they had done they had been punished tenfold and for every good action rewarded likewise. Those most terribly punished had been rulers who had committed crimes in pursuit of their ambitions, and such men, as they attempted at the end of their thousand years to return to earth, had been intercepted and carried off to torture.

Those souls, on the other hand, who were permitted to return to earth were shown a wide variety of lives, many more than there were souls present. They were then addressed by an interpreter who said, 'Your destiny will not be allotted to you; you must choose it. Virtue is free and as a man honours or dishonours her, he will have more or less of her. The responsibility for the choice is with the chooser. God is not to blame.'

There were laid out for inspection lives of every animal and of humans in every condition. The souls (both male and female) could choose lives which included supreme power in their cities, or distinction for beauty, or for success in athletics or for aristocratic birth, but mixed up in all the lives were elements of wealth and poverty and of disease and good health, as well as opportunities for either crime or virtue. As the souls came to choose, Er saw Agamemnon choosing the life of an eagle because he hated human nature, Orpheus choosing the life of a swan because he did not want to be born of a woman, since women had torn him apart. There were swans and other birds wanting to be humans. The last to choose was Odysseus. He had suffered too much in his previous life to want a life of successful ambition, so, finding with great difficulty the life of an obscure private individual, he gladly chose it.

Then the souls were made to drink from the River of Lethe, the river of forgetfulness, and after this they rose up like shooting stars to their next birth.

# HEROES FROM THE GLORIOUS PAST

## The Cretan story

Agenor was the king of Tyre, on the eastern edge of the great land-locked sea. Around him and behind him, to the south and east, were the powerful kingdoms of Asia where men were well established, active in trade and masters over a large part of the world. But gazing westward from the rim of Asia, the king looked over wide wastes towards little-known places untouched by the hand of fame. The gods ruled over all, but as yet they had not declared the destiny of these lands below.

Agenor had a daughter called Europa whose beauty attracted the all-seeing eye of Zeus. She and her maidens used to walk in the meadows where the cattle grazed, picking flowers and playing their gentle sports. One day Zeus approached them in the form of a white bull, for he was careful to disguise himself from Hera's watchful jealousy. The bull, which was a handsome and playful animal, mingled with the cattle and began to amuse the maidens. They petted him and hung him with garlands, and the bull seemed to encourage their tricks in such an eager and friendly way that at last Europa, the boldest of the girls, dared to climb up on his broad back. In a moment, the bull was off, galloping to the sea before a hand could reach out to save Europa. The bull plunged in and swam to the west, while Europa's companions stood on the shore and watched their princess being carried away, the flowers of a garland still clutched in her waving hand.

After swimming for a long time, the bull landed on the island of Crete. Then Zeus made himself known to Europa and possessed her in a grove of willows: and in due time she gave birth to three sons: Minos, Rhadamanthys and Sarpedon. Meanwhile in Tyre, Agenor lamented the loss of his daughter and he sent his wife and his sons out into the world to search for her. They travelled from land to land but could not find her, so they grew weary of the task and settled at last in strange places, raising new generations far from home.

In course of time, Zeus lost interest in Europa, abandoned her and went on his divine way. But King Asterius of Crete took pity on the girl and married her, accepting her children as his own and making them his heirs. The boys were proud, wilful fellows and when they grew up they began to quarrel. It was clear that they could not live together in peace and that two of them would have to leave. Minos proved himself the strongest of Europa's sons and he drove both his brothers out of Crete. Like the sons of Agenor, they went to other lands to settle and found cities, leaving Minos as sole heir to the Cretan throne. Minos married Pasiphaë, daughter of the sun god Helius, by whom he had many children, including two daughters called Ariadne and Phaedra.

When Asterius died, many opposed the succession of Minos, complaining that he was only an adopted son. Minos proudly replied that the gods had given him the right to the throne and offered to prove his case. He prayed to Poseidon to send a bull from the sea, as a sign of favour and promised that, if his request was granted, he would sacrifice the animal to the god. Poseidon granted the prayer, and the people accepted Minos as the god's choice. But the bull was so beautiful that the new king wanted to keep it. Instead of leading it to the altar, he tried to cheat, offering an inferior animal for the sacrifice. Poseidon was not deceived. In his anger, he devised an appropriate revenge, inflicting Pasiphaë with an unnatural lust for the bull.

Now there lived in Crete an Athenian called

Daedalus, who was the greatest craftsman in all the earth. He had been forced to flee from his native city because, in a fit of jealousy, he had killed a lad, who was both his nephew and his apprentice. At a tender age—some say he was only twelve years old—the boy showed signs of outstripping his master in skill. Not content with inventing a pair of compasses and the potter's wheel, he went on to make the first saw, inspired by the example of a fish's spine, or perhaps it was the jawbone of a crocodile. Such precocious genius was too much for Daedalus. He laid hold of his nephew and threw

## Crete and the Labyrinth

To Greeks who criticized the myths, the stories about Crete must have seemed even more unreal than they do to us. Thanks to the excavation of the palace of Cnossus we know that it was far larger and more elaborate than any building known to most Greeks. We know, too, from carvings and wall paintings, that bulls were important in the Cretan religion; and that teams of athletes gave displays of bull-leaping, probably as part of a religious ceremony. In these displays one of the athletes seized the horns of a bull and vaulted into a handstand on its back and from there to the ground, where another athlete stood waiting to catch him (or her—there were girl athletes as well as men). The story of the Minotaur, half bull, half man, may contain garbled memories of these displays.

What gave rise to the story of the Labyrinth? The name is not a word in the Greek language but may be connected with a Minoan word for a double axe, and double axes are carved on several walls of the palace. The palace was large and the remaining foundations show winding passages in which strangers might get lost. On the other hand, both Plutarch (who lived from about A D46 to about A D120) and Homer describe Cretan dances, one imitating the windings of the Labyrinth. Whether the story of Daedalus' Labyrinth represents the memory of the winding passages of a palace, or an intricate dance, or a maze, may never be finally established.

him into the sea, where his soul was changed by the gods into a partridge. This cruel murder shocked the Athenians. They arrested Daedalus and brought him before the court of the Areopagus, which condemned him to perpetual exile.

After some wanderings, Daedalus found his way to the palace of Minos, at Cnossus in Crete. The king received him well, glad to have the use of his legendary ingenuity and skill. Daedalus stayed, married and had a son called Icarus and all the time he remained the king's favourite, constructing for Minos many strange machines and designing wonderful buildings, the most marvellous of which was the maze, or Labyrinth, of Cnossus.

So when Queen Pasiphaë felt the sting of her ugly desire, not knowing how to satisfy her lust for the bull, she turned to Daedalus for help. Secretly, he made her a cunning model of a cow, a life-like form covered with hide and made to move with ingenious joints and levers. The queen fitted herself into the model which was then taken to the meadow and mingled with the herd. The bull mounted the imitation cow, and so Pasiphaë was shamefully satisfied. Nine months later her guilty secret was broadcast to the world when she gave birth to the Minotaur, a hideous monster with the head of a bull and the body of a man. King Minos was horrified. After consulting the oracle, he locked the Minotaur into the impenetrable Labyrinth which Daedalus had made.

Minos became a great and worthy king, establishing laws and good government, making Crete foremost among the lands of mankind. Zeus himself suggested the laws, and every nine years Minos was called to Mount Ida to give an account of himself to the Father of the Gods. And to help him in the work of government, Hephaestus built him a huge man of bronze, called Talos, who oversaw the laws, defended the shores with heavy missiles, and smothered invading soldiers in a fiery embrace. Even the gods acknowledged the fame of Minos. Zeus rescued him from the grip of Death and placed him in the Underworld as a Judge of the Dead, in recognition of the justice he had established in Crete.

# Theseus, King of Athens

While King Minos was bringing order to the land of Crete, making civilization flourish at Cnossus, and wielding the sword over his neighbours, another city was beginning to grow powerful across the sea to the north. On the broad, stony promontary of Attica, the city of Athens had been founded by Cecrops, a man sprung from the native soil; but the succession of its kings had plunged the people into turmoil. After many years of trouble and family grief, Aegeus, the son of an exiled king, invaded Attica and began to restore the fortunes of Athens.

King Aegeus, though twice-married, had no children, and he travelled to Delphi to ask the oracle how he might gain an heir. As was her custom, the priestess answered with a riddle, warning that he should not undo his wine-skin until he returned home. Aegeus was still puzzling over the riddle's meaning as he travelled back to Athens. At Corinth, where he rested, the witch Medea promised him her magical help, if Aegeus would offer her refuge in Athens. At Troezen, King Pittheus guessed the meaning of the oracle, made his guest drunk and put him to sleep in his daughter Aethra's bed. In the morning, Aegeus was ashamed of his drunken behaviour. He told Aethra that, if she gave birth to a son, she must not tell the boy the name of his father until he was well grown. To show when this might be, Aegeus explained that he would hide armour, weapons and a pair of sandals under a certain rock. Only when the son was strong enough to lift the rock should she divulge his true parentage.

In due time, a son was born and named Theseus. He developed so prodigiously that, when Pittheus spread the rumour that the lad's father was Poseidon, many believed him. Once, when the great hero, Heracles, visited Troezen, little Theseus, not yet ten, dared to face the snarling lion-skin he wore and was ready to attack it with an axe. At sixteen, Theseus was fully grown. He went to Delphi to dedicate a lock of hair to Apollo, then easily removed the rock which hid his father's gifts; and so he learned his father's name. Now he was ready to go to Athens, to claim his inheritance. The easiest route was by sea, but he insisted, despite his mother's pleas, on braving the dangers of the land journey, for he wished to be tested by such trials as his kinsman Heracles had met and overcome.

Theseus set out north for Athens, skirting the Saronic Sea. The road was rugged and menaced by as many terrors as any young hero could wish. At Epidaurus, he found the highway blocked by a lame robber clutching an enormous club. Theseus was too quick and agile for him. He left the robber dead but took the club for his own use. Then, crossing the Isthmus of Corinth, he came to the place where the giant Sinis tore travellers apart by binding them to two springy pine trees. Theseus forced the giant to bend down two trees and then served him with his own medicine. Next, Theseus left the direct path to hunt and kill the ferocious Grey Sow of Crommyon, and, on the high limestone cliffs of Megara, he made the way safe for travellers by defeating Sciron, a rogue who made those who passed by wash his feet and then kicked them over the cliff. Passing on to Eleusis, Theseus grappled with, and overcame, the wrestler Cercyon who crushed men to death in his pitiless arms. At the borders of Attica, Procrustes, 'the Stretcher', awaited him. This brigand had a bed on which he measured the unwary traveller. Those who were too long had their limbs shortened, and those who were too short were stretched to fit the bed. Theseus forced Procrustes on to his own bed, and made him fit. Then at last Theseus reached Athens. He purified himself at the wayside shrine and was ready to enter the city.

While Theseus was growing up in Troezen, Medea, who had promised Aegeus her magical help in return for refuge, took to her chariot drawn by winged dragons and fled to Athens. There, she bewitched old King Aegeus and married him, dominating his feeble old age. She had everything to fear from the arrival of Theseus and when her magic warned her that he had arrived in the city, she resolved to get rid of him. When he presented himself to the king, she offered him a poisonous drink and so, unwittingly, gave Theseus the chance to claim his inheritance. For Theseus was suspicious and drew his sword. At once Aegeus recognized the weapon as the one he had hidden in Troezen and, with tears and blessings, he took his son in his arms. Medea slunk away defeated, concealed by a magic cloud.

So Medea was driven out and Theseus took his rightful place at the king's side. He had not come a moment too soon, for Athens was full of troubles, both from Theseus' resentful cousins and from a raging bull which ravaged the country around Marathon. These Theseus could overcome, but other, greater troubles loomed.

The greatest calamity facing Athens was the cruel burden put on the people by King Minos of Crete. One of his sons had been killed in Attica and Minos advanced with fire and sword, determined to avenge the boy's death. Since Aegeus was too old and weak to resist, he submitted to the Cretan king, agreeing to pay each ninth year a tribute of seven youths and seven maidens. These Minos imprisoned in the Labyrinth at Cnossus, leaving them there to starve or be killed by the Minotaur. Twice Athens watched the sorrowful departure of her sons and daughters. At the third demand,

## Real time and legendary time

Myths and folktales are timeless. That is to say they exist in a sort of time-vacuum—the Australian aborigines call it 'the Dream-time'. They happen 'once upon a time'. Legends on the other hand, because they are related, however tenuously, to real events and real people can have a time-scale of sorts. For Greek legends this was provided by the Theban and Trojan wars. Theseus and two other heroes of the Theban war are all said to have had sons who fought at Troy, which Greek historians put in the twelfth or thirteenth centuries B C. Theseus, therefore, must have belonged to the generation before the Trojan war.

However, Theseus' most famous exploit is the killing of the Minotaur in the Labyrinth of Crete, and that does not fit either the real or the legendary time-frame. Minos and Cretan sea-power and the magnificent palace of Cnossus all belong to a period far further back (more like ten or twelve generations before the Trojan war) in real time. Even in the telescoped time of the legends the killing of the Minotaur must be three generations before the sack of Troy. Theseus (like King Arthur in mediaeval legend) seems to have become the hero (or villain) of many stories which had originally been told about other characters of legend, myth or folktale.

Every Greek knew the twelve labours of Heracles and how he had rid the earth of various deadly monsters which made life dangerous for humans. The fashion which appears in the late sixth century for Athenian vases which depict Theseus disposing of picturesque ruffians on the road to Athens suggests to suspicious scholars that some Athenians were deliberately attributing to their legendary king exploits, not originally his, to rival those of Heracles.

Nearly three centuries after the Greeks had been conquered by the Romans and had become peaceful subjects of the Roman Empire, a Greek named Plutarch wrote biographies of famous Greeks and Romans. Nearly all of these were historical characters. When he decided to write the life of Theseus, Plutarch was aware that he was dealing with many incredible and contradictory fables, but he does his best to distil from these something that looks like history. It is, of course, nothing of the sort, but it does give a useful idea of what the average Athenian liked to believe about the legendary founder of their unified state. Plutarch's biographies are full of delightful anecdotes and were widely read, in an excellent translation, in Elizabethan times. Shakespeare knew them well and used them for many of his plays. The biography of Theseus, for example, provides the setting for *A Midsummer Nights Dream*.

when the citizens wept and blamed their king, Theseus offered himself as one of the victims, vowing that he would kill the Minotaur and bring back the seven youths and maidens. And as a sign of success, he promised to hoist white sails as he returned, instead of the usual black sails of grief.

When the ship reached Crete, Minos, not content with sending the Athenians to their deaths, also desired one of the maidens. Theseus intervened. Strong words passed between the two men, leading to boasting and challenges. Minos claimed kinship with Zeus, and in confirmation the mighty Thunderer made the sky roar. Theseus replied, swearing by Poseidon's name. But Minos contemptuously tossed a ring in the sea, daring Theseus that the sea god would not allow him to retrieve it. At once, Theseus dived into the water, where a friendly dolphin carried him down to Poseidon's palace in the deep. There, Poseidon showed him his great favour: not only was the ring returned to him, but Poseidon granted him three wishes for the future.

Despite this mark of divine favour, Theseus was paraded in the streets with the other victims destined for the Minotaur. There the king's daughter, Ariadne, saw him and fell instantly in love. That night she approached the prison where he awaited his fate and promised that she would show him how to escape from the Labyrinth if he would take her to Athens as his wife. Theseus gave his word and she handed him a large ball of thread and explained the trick which Daedalus, the Labyrinth's architect, had once taught her. Then she stole away to make her preparations.

Next morning, when the gate of the maze clanged behind the doomed Athenians, Theseus took the ball of thread, fastened one end to the lintel and let the thread unwind as he wandered here and there in the tortuous passages. Somewhere deep in the interior he came upon the sleeping Minotaur. Taking the beast by the hair, Theseus dragged it to its feet and, though it fought wildly, with all its brutish strength, he killed it with his bare hands and offered it as a sacrifice to Poseidon; then he pulled in the thread and, step by

step, retraced his way to the gate. Ariadne was waiting there with the young Athenians and knew by the blood on his clothes that the deed was done. She had prepared everything for their flight. Quickly, they made for the harbour, where a ship lay waiting, the rowers already bent over their oars. As they clambered aboard, the oars bit the water and the ship was out on the sea before the alarm could be raised.

With this good start, the Athenians came safely to the island of Naxos, where they stopped to rest. Then, for a reason which only the gods know, Theseus continued the journey without Ariadne. Some say his heart was caught by another woman, and others that he feared what the people of Athens might do to Ariadne, the enemy princess. Still others blamed Dionysus who (they claimed) deceived Theseus with a vision and sent him away in a state of forgetfulness, so that Dionysus himself could take Ariadne and marry her.

From Naxos, Theseus sailed on to Delos, pausing there for sacrifices and celebratory games. But when the ship approached the harbour, Theseus was in such a joyous mood that he quite forgot to hoist the white sails that signalled his success. Old Aegeus was keeping watch upon the cliff-top, strained with anxiety. He saw the black sails bellying in the wind and he despaired. Believing his only son was lost forever, he threw himself into the sea, which ever after has been called the Aegean in his honour.

When King Minos discovered that his prisoners and his daughter had escaped, he knew at once that only Daedalus, the inventor, could have helped them. Full of wrath, he imprisoned Daedalus, with his son Icarus, in the Labyrinth he had built. Its gates were closely guarded and its high walls too steep to climb; so Daedalus, watching the birds flying freely far above, decided to imitate their flight. He constructed two large pairs of wings from feathers, cord and wax. When the wings were ready, he strapped one pair to his arms, the other to his son's and gave Icarus his instructions: 'My son, do not fly too high, or the fire of Helius will melt the wax; nor too low, or the spray of the

## Theseus in Crete

Just as the story of the Minotaur may contain garbled memories of Cretan bull-leaping, so the demand for seven girls and seven boys from Athens may contain a memory of a time when Athens was obliged to pay tribute to Minos.

Between 2000 and 1400 B C Cretan colonies were planted on many of the Aegean islands and possibly on the mainland also, so Crete could well have been capable of imposing a tribute—or a demand for hostages—on the ruler of Athens.

## Theseus, Phaedra and Hippolytus

The story of Theseus, Phaedra and Hippolytus has long haunted the imagination of poets and playwrights. Though all three characters existed in myth, and had many legends told about them, the actual plot seems to have been the creation of the playwright Euripides. One myth was remembered in an ancient ritual enacted in the city of Troezen (Theseus' birthplace). There girls who were about to be married dedicated a lock of their hair to a divine hero named Hippolytus. Another myth, which Euripides may have known, concerned a young man with whom Aphrodite herself fell in love but who was killed in a hunting accident. There were at least two other legends similar to the story of Phaedra and Hippolytus. Out of these, or similar materials, Euripides created a dramatic masterpiece—the tragedy named the *Hippolytus*. On the human level it is the story of a woman's obsessive passion for her stepson, a young man's puritanical rejection of sex and women, and of a father who by an overhasty curse brings about the death of his innocent son. On the divine level it is the story of the jealous rivalry of two goddesses and their callous manipulation of human beings to spite one another. On a third level the play is about the frailty of human happiness. In his play, Euripides is raising questions about religion and the Olympian gods and the nature of human life.

waves will make the feathers heavy with salt water and you will fall.'

At dawn they set off, flapping nobly upward, rising out of the maze, flying high above the startled guards, so that men were amazed and took them for gods. Below them, islands were like emeralds and water sparkled, and in this zestful freedom Icarus soared higher and higher towards the sun. As Daedalus had warned, the sun's heat blazed in the cloudless sky, and the wax began to drip; one by one, feathers began to fall from the frame, drifting past Daedalus as he flew below. In a cloud of feathers, Icarus plunged to his death close by the island called Icaria in his memory.

With long, cautious strokes Daedalus flew sadly on, putting Crete and its horrors far behind, alighting finally in Sicily, in the land of King Cocalus, where his famous talent made him welcome.

Now Theseus became king of Athens, forging the peoples of Attica into a strong confederation under his leadership. And this leadership was soon put to the test by an invasion of Amazons. It is said that he provoked these warrior women by raiding their territory, then seizing and marrying their queen, Antiope. In retaliation, the Amazons swept out of the frozen north and besieged the Acropolis. They sacrificed to Ares, the god of war, on the hill called Areopagus, but Ares seemed not to hear their prayer, for the Athenians defeated them. Some say Antiope fought her own people by her husband Theseus' side and was killed by a javelin. But others claim that Theseus, fickle as always in matters of love, set her aside to marry Ariadne's sister Phaedra.

Whatever is the truth of this sad marriage, it is certain that Antiope, the Amazon, bore Theseus a son named Hippolytus. This youth cared only for hunting. He was completely devoted to chaste Artemis, the goddess of the hunt, and would have nothing to do with mortal women. Such coldness towards the powers of love affronted Aphrodite and she decided to make Hippolytus suffer for his indifference. One day when he was officiating in the temple, wearing the robe of the priest and with

his hair in garlands, Aphrodite out of spite caused Phaedra, Theseus' wife, to fall in love with him. Phaedra, shocked and disgusted by her forbidden love, hid her passion from him. But passion sent by the gods cannot be concealed forever. Her nurse, thinking to save her from unhappiness, told Hippolytus the truth. He was as horrified as Phaedra by the situation and met her with harsh words of accusation. In a frenzy between rage and desire, Phaedra tore her clothes and hanged herself. Before she died, however, she left a message for her husband, accusing Hippolytus and blaming him bitterly for her fate.

When Theseus read the message, and learned of his wife's cruel death, he banished his son and cursed him angrily in Poseidon's name. Poseidon, who, long ago below the sea had promised Theseus three wishes, now counted this curse as one of them. As Hippolytus' chariot fled from Athens along the seashore, Poseidon sent a monstrous white bull out of the water. It charged towards the frightened horses, making them rear and bolt, flinging Hippolytus to the ground. Still tangled in the reins, he was dragged to his death behind the panicky hooves.

The life of Theseus, which had begun in such a blaze of hope and achievement, ended in darkness and failure. In his middle age he formed a friendship with the disreputable Peirithous, who soon led him astray. Their most dangerous plan, among many disgraceful undertakings, was to seize Persephone from the Underworld, to make her the bride of Peirithous. Hades, of course, easily foiled this brazen plot and lashed the conspirators to the Seat of Forgetfulness, where they were menaced by hissing snakes and tortured by Furies. After four years, Heracles pulled Theseus free, but Peirithous was abandoned to eternal suffering.

On his return to Athens, Theseus found the city looted and the people muttering against the folly of their king. Rebellion blazed and Theseus was driven out. He found refuge on the island of Scyros and died there, ignominiously, in exile: the friend of Heracles, the conqueror of the Minotaur, was kicked over a cliff by the royal servants.

# Oedipus and the city of Thebes

Before the founding of the cities, when the children of Agenor first went out into the world in search of their lost sister Europa, Cadmus, her brother, travelled with his mother first to Thrace. His mother died in that wild country and Cadmus, uncertain how to proceed, set out for Delphi to consult the oracle. Through the mouth of the priestess, Apollo told him to abandon the quest for Europa. Instead, he was to follow a cow until it lay down to rest and there found a city.

Cadmus took the road east to Boeotia, driving before him a cow with a moonmark on its flank. By a pleasant hill in the heart of the land the cow sank down exhausted, and Cadmus prepared to sacrifice it to Athene. Water was needed for the ritual and Cadmus sent his men to fetch it from a spring. The stream, however, was guarded by a dragon, dedicated to Ares, and before the men had time to draw their swords, the dragon guardian killed them all. Cadmus, in revenge, crushed its head with a large rock. When the sacrifice was complete, Athene appeared. 'Gather the dragon's teeth,' she commanded, 'and sow them like grain upon the ground.'

Cadmus, wondering, obeyed and at once, a host of armed men sprang up, clashing their weapons in the air. These were the Sparti, 'the Sown Men'. Afraid of their fierce looks, Cadmus hurled stones among them, and the soldiers, confused, turned to fight each other, attacking so fiercely that soon only five were left alive.

With these five soldiers, Athene told Cadmus to build a city and there, on the spot where the cow had fallen, he founded the city of Thebes. Now the gods smiled on Cadmus and his enterprise: he married Harmonia, daughter of Ares and Aphrodite, and all the gods of Olympus attended the wedding feast.

Thebes started with the blessing of the gods, but like many early cities, it soon began to shake with family discord. Cadmus and Harmonia abdicated

and their descendants could not hold the inheritance together. Some were killed, some banished. Laius, son of Labdacus, regained the city, but he returned from exile under a curse, a fatal burden destined to pass to all the royal line of Thebes.

King Laius married Iocaste, and, in due time, a baby son was born. Instead of bringing joy, this birth brought sadness for the Delphic oracle had given them a tragic warning: Iocaste's son was destined to destroy his father. So Laius took the boy, put a spike through his feet, and sent a servant to leave him to die of cold and hunger on the hillside of Mount Cithaeron. The baby, however, did not die. Instead, he was found by a shepherd from Corinth, who took the pitiful little bundle back to his king. Moved by the plight of the baby and having no children of their own, King Polybus and his wife accepted the child with joy. They named him Oedipus, or 'Swell-foot', because of his wounded feet.

Polybus raised Oedipus as his son. The youth grew well and was happy in Corinth, although from time to time he heard disquieting whispers about his parentage. When he was full-grown, he decided to question the oracle at Delphi. The answer of the priestess frightened him very much:

he was never to enter his native land, for if he did, he would kill his father and marry his mother. In horror, Oedipus turned his back on Corinth, the only home he knew. But no man can circumvent the decree of the gods. At a place called the Divided Roads, he found his path blocked by King Laius in a chariot. Of course, the two proud men did not know each other, and neither would give way. When the argument turned into a fight, young Oedipus killed his unknown father with his sword.

Oedipus continued on his way to Thebes, where news of the king's death, by an unknown hand, had preceded him. The city was in alarm and Queen Iocaste's brother, Creon, was trying to calm the worried citizens. To add to the confusion in the city, the Sphinx was menacing the countryside around, making it difficult either to enter or to leave. This monster, with a woman's head, a lion's body, a snake's tail, and eagle's wings, stopped all travellers with a riddle, and those who could not answer were devoured. So many people were destroyed that Creon in desperation offered the hand of the widowed Queen Iocaste to anyone who could answer the riddle and send the Sphinx away.

With the confidence of youth, Oedipus went out

to face the monster. 'What,' demanded the Sphinx, preparing to tear apart this puny being who dared to match wits with her, 'walks on four legs in the morning, two legs in the afternoon, and three in the evening?' But Oedipus promptly replied: 'The answer is man, who crawls on all fours as a baby, walks upright in maturity, and hobbles with a stick in his old age.'

Because he had solved the riddle, the furious Sphinx spread its vast wings and took off into the air from a cliff-top, never to return. Oedipus accepted his reward and married Iocaste. Thus, in all ignorance he married his mother as the oracle had foretold, an act of impiety intolerable to the gods.

For many years Oedipus reigned well and happily in Thebes. With Iocaste he had two sons, Eteocles and Polyneices, and two daughters, Antigone and Ismene. It seemed that the gods were blind to his unconscious sin; but such a crime cannot go unpunished and eventually the gods sent a plague and a famine on the land. When no-one could guess the cause, and the oracle was consulted, the priestess replied: 'Expel the murderer of Laius'. Who was this villain? Laius had been killed obscurely, by some forgotten wayside, long ago. The plague and famine raged unchecked.

Then old King Polybus died in Corinth and a messenger came to offer Oedipus the crown. Oedipus dared not accept, for he still feared he might marry his mother, as the Delphic oracle had foretold. And now the curse of Thebes began to take its baneful course. 'Why', said the messenger, 'have no fear. Merope is not your mother. You were an adopted son.' Then the full terrible story came out, and was confirmed by the aged palace servant who had taken the baby Oedipus to Mount Cithaeron. In despair, Oedipus put out his own eyes, while poor Iocaste, looking back on the black years of her incest, hanged herself.

Banished from Thebes by the order of Creon, Oedipus wandered away, but not before he had cursed his two ill-gotten sons, who watched him go without remorse. Only his faithful daughter Antigone went with him, a hand to guide his blind

steps. After many journeys in exile they came at last to Colonus, in Attica. There, at the shrine of the Eumenides, he made offerings to the avenging Furies and was released from the wrath of the gods. Reconciled and finally at peace, Oedipus knew that his end was near. He summoned his two daughters, took leave of them, and slipped quietly out of this life.

When the sons of Oedipus became men, they shared the kingship of Thebes and agreed to rule alternately, year by year. The first term fell to Eteocles, but when his year was over he broke his word and refused to hand the kingship to his brother. Polyneices went to Argos in a rage. There he married King Adrastus' daughter and, with the king's help, set out to regain his rightful kingdom.

Adrastus gathered seven powerful warriors to fight against Thebes and outlined his campaign. Only one, Amphiaraus, was unwilling to go, for he had the gift of prophecy and, through this, could see the failure of the expedition. However, Polyneices bribed his wife and she persuaded her husband to go with them. Amphiaraus set out reluctantly and, full of resentment against his wife, he charged his sons to murder her if he should be killed, and to take up the fight against Thebes when their time came.

Then Adrastus set out from Argos with the brave band of allies, those whom we later called the Seven Against Thebes. Under the walls of Thebes, the herald blew his trumpet and demanded that Eteocles hand over the city. Then the seven

## Greek tragedy

Greek tragedies were more like grand opera, or sacred oratorios, than like a play by Shakespeare or any modern playwright. As with grand opera there was a Chorus who sang and danced, and the behaviour of the actors on the stage was very unlike the way anyone would behave in real life. As with oratorios religious feeling is an essential element in the composer's (or author's) inspiration—even though many of the audience may take a purely aesthetic interest in the performance. Additionally in Greek tragedy the difference between the actions on the stage and the events of real life is emphasized by the masks which all the actors wear.

Although the plays of Aeschylus, Sophocles, and Euripides are always referred to as 'Greek' tragedies, it would be more accurate to call them 'Athenian' tragedies. A little, but not much, is known about the origins and early development of tragedy as a form of art. Whether or not it originated elsewhere than at Athens, it was at Athens that from about 530 B C onwards the yearly festival of Dionysus included a dramatic competition in honour of the god. From all the entrants three playwrights were selected to present each a programme of three tragedies and one satyr play. The festival was organized by the state of Athens

and attendance at the open-air theatre was free—it was part of a religious ceremony. Large numbers of citizens of all classes came to watch and hear. Very many plays have been lost, including all those performed before the middle years of the fifth century B C. The early plays had only one actor. Aeschylus made it two and Sophocles three: but each actor could play several parts by wearing a different mask and assuming a different voice. At first the singing, dancing and speeches of the chorus (at first fifteen members, later twelve) were of great importance. During the fifth century, especially in the case of Euripides, the playwrights became more concerned with human, and less with religious problems. Nevertheless, with one exception, all the surviving tragedies have plots based on the myths.

The satyr plays (only one has survived complete) had a chorus of Satyrs—lewd, rustic creatures half-beast, half-human, with horses' tails. The humour of the plays was bawdy, reinforcing the theory that they originated in fertility rites. Greek comedies were performed in much the same way as tragedies, with masks, a chorus and singing and dancing. However, the plots were not usually taken from the myths although there are many references to mythical characters and events.

champions took their stations before the seven gates and prepared to attack. Eteocles was unmoved but Creon's son, believing that his death would save the city, sacrificed himself to Ares, god of war.

The fight was long and bloody. Capaneus, one of the Seven, scaled the walls, swearing that not even Zeus could hold him back. Immediately, the Thunderer killed him with a lightning bolt. Another champion, Tydeus, fought so bravely, though mortally wounded, that Athene wished to preserve his life. But when she found him, in a mad rage, gnawing the head of an enemy, she let him die in disgust. The tide began to turn against the invaders. The brothers Eteocles and Polyneices killed each other in hand-to-hand combat.

Amphiaraus, fleeing from a rain of missiles, was swallowed by the earth. Of all the champions of Argos, only King Adrastus survived, carried beyond all pursuers by his winged horse Arion.

Once more, Thebes was without a king and again Creon surveyed the broken city. As he stood among the dead and brooded on the damage done to Thebes he made a stern decree: the Theban dead should be buried with honours, but no-one should touch the bodies of the Seven, which must be left to the crows and the scavenging dogs. This was a terrible justice, for it condemned the spirits of the unburied to wander the earth forever without hope of release into the afterlife. But gentle Antigone could not leave her brother Polyneices in this sad state, even though he had spurned his father

## The Theban plays

In Homer's *Odyssey*, among the famous women seen by Odysseus when he visits the underworld is 'fair Epicaste, mother of Oedipodes, who unknowingly committed a great crime, marrying her own son' but 'the gods revealed everything…and she came to the House of Hades, having hanged herself from a high beam, overcome by her own sorrow.'

Three centuries later, out of the same story, the playwright Sophocles composed another tragedy that has haunted the imagination of posterity: *Oedipus Tyrannus* or *Oedipus the King*—perhaps the most famous of all the tragedies that have survived from ancient times. Its fame in this century is partly due to the psychoanalyst Sigmund Freud, who made its plot the basis of his best-known book *The Interpretation of Dreams* and named one of the neurotic conditions he described 'The Oedipus complex'.

Sophocles wrote 123 plays but only seven survive. Of these, three concern Oedipus and his family misfortunes. The harsh decree of Creon that the body of Polyneices, who led the seven heroes to attack Thebes, should be left unburied, was the subject of a lost play by Aeschylus, and a surviving play by Euripides. In Sophocles' tragedy on the same legendary episode, the *Antigone*, he concentrated on

the determination of Oedipus' daughter Antigone to give the body of her brother Polyneices a form of burial, even at the cost of her life. In the play Creon represents patriotism and the authority of the state: Antigone represents compassion and the bidding of her conscience—or rather that is one element of the clash between them, for this must be one of the most frequently analysed tragedies of all time. As one modern scholar wrote, 'It can honestly be said that after twenty-five centuries we are still debating the precise meaning of the conflict between Antigone and Creon.'

As an illustration of this, it is known that during the Second World War, the censorship department of the German Gestapo had to decide whether to permit the performance in Paris of a certain play newly written by a French playwright. This play was a reworking of the plot of Sophocles' *Antigone* with exactly the same characters and the same story. The censors had to decide whether the play would encourage or discourage French men and women who were thinking of risking their lives by joining the Resistance Movement. The censors decided in the end to permit performances but there can be little doubt that many in the audiences saw the play as an encouragement to join the Resistance, just as Antigone had resisted the harsh decision of Creon.

Oedipus and raised his hand against his own people. She walked out fearlessly among the dead to sprinkle a little dust on his body, a token act of burial. When Creon heard of this pious act, he angrily ordered her to be sealed inside a burial chamber, to die alone in airless dark. Haemon, Creon's son, who loved Antigone, pleaded for her life and in the market-place the blind prophet Teiresias denounced this savage deed. At last Creon repented—but too late. When his soldiers rushed to the tomb to release her, Haemon was dead by its door and Antigone had hanged herself

Thus the curse which, so many years before, Laius had brought to the House of Thebes, worked its inevitable havoc from father to son. Nor was the unlucky tale complete. The sons of Amphiaraus, true to the oath made to their father, took up the struggle against Thebes. Their war was the war of the Epigoni, 'the Later-Born', and they succeeded where their fathers had failed. They sacked the city, razed the walls and took their booty home, driving the conquered people out to virgin country and a new home. The Epigoni returned in triumph, but now the son of Amphiaraus faced his father's final order: that he should kill his mother. Torn between the opposing demands of filial piety and filial sacrilege, he braved himself to obey. Though Apollo approved the deed, the son could not escape the vengeance of the Furies, and the primeval avengers hounded him through many years of family grief to a miserable death in a roadside ambush.

At last, the slate was wiped clean. The implacable decision of the gods against the House of Thebes, which no mortal could avoid, had claimed its final victim.

## Greek women

Women play an important role in Greek myths but a very small role in Greek history. The conditions of life of women in Ancient Greece seem to have varied from place to place and from one period to another, and it is only about the women of Athens that we have any reliable written evidence—and that was written by men. There were no Athenian Jane Austens or Charlotte Brontes. Other evidence comes from paintings on Athenian vases and archaeological reconstructions of a few houses in Attica. Such evidence as there is suggests that respectable upper and middle class Athenian women led very restricted and secluded lives, largely confined to their homes, and not just to their homes but to their own quarters within their homes. They did not meet their husbands' men friends nor were they present at his banquets which took place in a special 'men's room' (an invariable feature of all but the poorest houses). There were no professions open to respectable women though a few of them performed public roles as priestesses.

Apart from the wives and daughters of Athenian citizens there were in Athens many female slaves and free foreign women who had no rights as citizens and could not marry a citizen. Many of the slave women were domestic servants, but some female slaves and some foreign women were professional entertainers who attended banquets to play the flute and sing and be available as prostitutes if required. Other such women entertained men in their own homes.

The Athenian playwrights had no knowledge of how women had lived in Minoan or Mycenaean times, so Minoan or Mycenaean princesses like Phaedra or Antigone are portrayed as if they were living under more or less the same conditions as fifth century Athenian women. The wife of an Athenian citizen who became involved in an extra-marital love affair disgraced herself and her sex: the wife of an Athenian citizen who fell in love with her stepson could only be regarded as depraved. Euripides, in trying to win his audience's sympathy and understanding for Phaedra, was defying conventional Athenian morality and many Athenians were shocked. During his lifetime Euripides won very few first prizes for his plays, but later generations of Greeks found them more to their taste than the less realistic, more dignified plays of Aeschylus and Sophocles which had been less disturbing to fifth century ideas of morality.

# THE ACCURSED

## Perseus and the Gorgon

In the mists of the past, when the first men inhabited the world, the great gods of Olympus were angry with the river god Inachus. This insignificant deity, of small importance in the wider world, looked after the rivers and streams of Argos, and had been chosen to judge whether his country belonged to Poseidon or Hera. No decision could be right, or simple, for to favour one risked the hatred of the other. When Inachus gave the prize to Hera, Poseidon sent a drought which ever after made the streams run dry in summer. It was a bad beginning for the land of Argos.

The enmity of Poseidon was a hard penance, but soon Hera herself was also angry with the family of the river god, for Zeus, in his usual wilful way, fell in love with the river god's daughter, Io, who served as a priestess in Hera's temple. Knowing well the divine trouble he could expect from his wife, Zeus denied his passion, submissively turning Io into a white heifer which Hera led away and gave to the all-seeing Argus Panoptes for safekeeping. This monster, with a hundred watchful eyes, tethered Io in an olive grove at Mycenae, and Hera felt secure. Great Zeus was not deterred from his pursuit; he had only pretended to submit to Hera's will and now he sent Hermes to steal Io back for him. Argus, the watchful, was difficult to deceive, for some, at least, of his hundred eyes, were always open, always vigilant. Hermes, however, lulled him fast asleep with soulful music; then, when every eye was closed, he slew the sleeping monster, quietly untied the heifer and set her free. Now Hera was more angry than ever. As a reproach to Zeus and Hermes, she rescued the eyes of Argus and placed them in the beautiful tail of the peacock, then sent a vengeful cloud of gadflies to chase Io all over the world.

Io galloped onward, driven from land to land by the merciless sting of the flies. She fled over the Ionian Sea, which still bears her name, north to the Danube, then around the Black Sea and over the Bosphorus. Still the flies followed after her, pursuing her all the way to India, and back again, by way of Ethiopia and the long valley of the Nile, to northern Africa. At last, she was allowed to rest. Zeus restored her to her human form and she gave birth to his son, Epaphus. For a time there was peace. The family of Io prospered on the hot southern shore of the inland sea and brought forth in the course of years two grandsons for Epaphus, named Agenor and Belus.

The sons of Agenor travelled and colonized far afield, in Crete and Thebes and Athens, but fate drove the children of Belus back to the ancestral home in Argos and the country round about. Belus himself had two sons, Danaus and Aegyptus, who, when they became men, both ruled kingdoms of their own. Danaus had fifty daughters, and Aegyptus fifty sons. After the death of their father, the brothers fell out over their inheritance, a quarrel which Aegyptus tried to settle by offering his fifty sons in marriage to his brother's fifty daughters. Danaus, suspecting a plot, fled with all his family to Argos, and, with the aid of signs and portents, persuaded the people that he was their rightful king. When Danaus was established in Argos, Aegyptus sent his fifty sons to claim their brides. At first, Danaus refused, but when the young men besieged the city he reluctantly gave his consent. The marriages were celebrated but none was destined to survive. That night, acting on Danaus' orders, each bride murdered her new husband in his bed. Only Hypermnestra was too tender-hearted to do the terrible deed and she allowed her husband Lynceus to escape.

Danaus paid for his deceit for he died without an heir and the kingship passed to Lynceus, the sole surviving son of Aegyptus: so after all, the second branch of the family of Belus inherited the land of Argos. Two generations passed in peace before the twins Proetus and Acrisius were born and trouble came again to Argos. These princes fought even in the womb and, as they grew, they quarrelled so much that no one place could hold them both. Eventually they agreed to share the kingdom: Acrisius reigned in Argos, while Proetus took Tiryns as his share. There, seven giant masons of the family of the Cyclopes, built the fortress walls, piling the mighty stones so skilfully that they stand there to this day, a wonder to all later generations of more puny folk.

Acrisius had one child, a pretty daughter Danaë, but no male heir. Worried by the lack of a son, he consulted an oracle, but the answer was far from reassuring: 'You will have no son, and you will die by your grandson's hand,' the oracle intoned. Acrisius was determined to prevent this calamity and, defying the power of the Fates, he locked Danaë into a bronze dungeon, setting fierce dogs around the door so that no man would dare to enter. But Zeus, whose eye was forever open for a pretty maiden, saw her distress and appeared within her prison as a shower of gold. Their son, born in captivity, was Perseus.

Acrisius was angry and afraid. Not daring to kill his own child, he put mother and baby in a wooden chest and cast them out to sea. Wind and tide carried the chest to the isle of Seriphos where a man walking on the shore heard the baby's bawling cries, broke open the chest and led the sorry couple to King Polydectes. The king accepted mother and child into his house and raised Perseus as if he were his own son.

From the first, Polydectes desired to marry Danaë, but she would have nothing to do with his attentions. Perseus defended his mother's wishes as much as he was able and, while he was a child, Polydectes ignored his boyish interference. As he grew to manhood, however, his presence became

first an irritation, then a threat. Still wanting the mother but afraid to antagonize her bold son, Polydectes devised a cunning way of removing Perseus from the island. Pretending that he wished to marry another woman, he called on all his nobles to bring him wedding gifts. The other nobles brought fine horses, but Perseus had nothing of his own to give. Recklessly, he offered Polydectes anything he wished for, 'even the head of the Gorgon Medusa herself!' he boasted. The king accepted immediately.

Perseus set off sadly, not knowing what to do to make good his promise. But Athene, the grey-eyed, came quickly to his side. She was the sworn enemy of the Gorgon Medusa, who had, in distant times, offended her. Medusa was the most hideous of the three Gorgon sisters, daughters of the sea. Instead of arms, she had a monster's leathery wings, with claws of brass in place of hands. Upon her head grew writhing serpents, flicking their venomous fangs and hissing ceaselessly. No man could meet Medusa's gaze and live, for her fierce eyes turned everyone she looked upon to stone. To save him from this fate, the grey-eyed goddess gave Perseus a shield of polished metal so that he could watch Medusa in reflection, protected from her dangerous eyes. Hermes provided him with a sickle made of adamantine, which cut the hardest substance at a single stroke. Athene also told him of three further things to help him in his dangerous task: a pair of winged sandals, a magic pouch and Hades' helmet of invisibility. To find these, she told him, he must consult the Graeae. These strange sea-creatures, grey-haired from birth, now shared between them only one single eye and tooth. At first, out of some ancient malevolence, they would not answer Perseus' request. But Perseus crept among them and snatched the single eye and tooth as they were passed around, refusing to return them until the hags told him what he wanted.

Perseus collected the sandals, the pouch and Hades' dog-skin cap and prayed to Athene for victory. Then, airborne on the winged sandals he flew to the edge of Oceanus, where, amid the twisted rocks of the Hyperborean land, the rain wept down on the grotesque figures of the Gorgons. The dreadful sisters were asleep when Perseus dropped noiselessly from the air. Gazing into his shield, he carefully picked out Medusa, the only one of the three who was mortal and could therefore die. There she lay, tusks growing from her mouth and her scalp writhing with watchful serpents. Still turning away his eyes, Perseus struck the head off with a single blow and caught it in his magic pouch.

The task was done and it was time to be away as quickly as possible. Perseus put on Hades' cap of invisibility and, with Medusa's head sealed in the magic pouch, launched himself into the air. The sisters of Medusa were awake and screaming for revenge, but they could see no-one, for Perseus was invisible. Pursued by their angry cries, he flew south and east, following the North African coast. Some say he showed the Gorgon's head to Atlas as he passed, turning that weary giant who upheld the sky into a mountain. And, as he flew across Libya, the drops of blood that fell from his pouch onto the desert created the many poisonous snakes that infest those wastelands.

Continuing his flight towards Ethiopia, Perseus saw beneath him a woman chained to a rock on the shore. As he circled above, he saw in the distance a sea-serpent, beating its way towards her. A man and woman stood on the cliff-top above her, staring anxiously at the sea. Struck by the maiden's beauty and her desperate situation, Perseus landed beside them to ask what he could do to save her. Weeping, the woman told him the sad tale. She was Cassiopeia, wife of King Cepheus. The maiden was her daughter, Andromeda. Queen Cassiopeia had unwisely boasted of a family beauty that was greater than that of the sea nymphs, and, to teach the queen humility, Poseidon had sent a sea serpent to devastate the land. Only the sacrifice of her daughter Andromeda would appease the monster and save the kingdom.

Perseus, who had loved Andromeda as soon as he saw her, promised to rescue her if he might marry her. The king and queen agreed immediately and Perseus leaped from the cliff and up into the air. The sea-serpent had almost reached Andromeda when it saw Perseus' shadow on the water and turned its attention from its prey to attack this silent challenger. Perseus saw his chance and with his adamantine sickle slashed off the monster's head.

The first part of the bargain was easier to fulfil than the second, for Andromeda was already betrothed to another man and he was not easily or peacefully displaced. At last, however, the marriage was celebrated and Perseus returned to Seriphos with his bride. The fearful Gorgon's head still lay safe within his magic pouch.

When Perseus arrived in Seriphos, he found his mother Danaë was still in great danger from Polydectes, who, since she still refused him, had shut her in a temple to choose between marriage and starvation. Polydectes himself was feasting with his friends and greeted Perseus with insolent disdain.
'I've come to redeem my promise,' cried Perseus and, covering his own eyes, held high the head of Medusa. The king and his court stared into the Gorgon's eyes and turned at once into a circle of stones, some standing, some reclining as each had been positioned at the feast.

With Danaë released, Perseus' great work was complete. He returned the winged sandals, the pouch and Hades' cap and gave the death-dealing head of Medusa to Athene, to wear upon her shield. Then, with nothing further to detain him in Seriphos, he sailed away to his native Argos. On his arrival, King Acrisius remembered the oracle's warning words and fled in panic to Larissa. There he lived quietly, thinking himself well away from his ill-omened grandson.

It was not long before the king of Larissa died and princes from far and wide were invited to the ceremonies held in his honour. Unknown to his grandfather, Perseus was one of those who came to compete at the funeral games. Taking his turn at the discus, he hurled it into the air; but when he threw it, the wind caught it and skimmed it into the watching crowd, where it struck Acrisius on

the head and killed him, as the oracle had ordained.

In remorse, Perseus left Argos and took the second city of Tiryns in exchange. There, he became a great and energetic king, founding new cities at Midea and Mycenae, and eventually joining the two kingdoms of Tiryns and Argos so that the whole of Argolis was one powerful land.

## Heroes and ancestors

The story of Perseus' adventures is more of a folktale than most Greek myths. Heroes with impossible tasks to accomplish provide the starting point for many fireside tales—tales in which the tasks are nonetheless accomplished with the help of fairies, wise old women, sympathetic animals or magical aids such as Perseus' cap of invisibility, winged sandals and adamantine blade. Today the magical aids have been technologically updated for James Bond, Batman, and other film, or TV heroes.

The head of Medusa, portrayed with her tongue sticking out, was a favourite device for frightening away evil beings from temples—like the gargoyles on mediaeval cathedrals.

The historian Herodotus seems to have taken seriously the story that Perseus was the ancestor of the Persians. He reports a story (which he does not himself wholly believe) that the Persian king Xerxes, before his invasion of Greece, sent an envoy to Argos reminding the Argives that, as a Persian, he was descended from their King Perseus and therefore they should not fight against him. This was the reason—so the story said—why the Argives remained neutral during the Persian wars.

Scholars do not yet know for certain where the Medes and the Persians came from but from archaeological evidence and the evidence of language, it seems likely that they came by slow stages from somewhere north and east of the Caspian Sea. The Greeks knew nothing about the migrations of the early tribes but were very familiar with the stories of Jason's wife, Medea, and of Perseus the Gorgon-slayer. So they made Medea the ancestor of the Medes and Perseus of the Persians.

# Bellerophon and the Chimaera

While the children of Belus were making their home in and around Argos, the family of Sisyphus was established a little to the north, in the city of Corinth. Sisyphus, the mortal who dared to defy Zeus and who tricked Death for a time, finally went to the everlasting punishment that awaited him in Tartarus and left the kingdom to his son Glaucus. Glaucus was no more fortunate than his father: during a chariot race at the Isthmian games, his horses, maddened by eating magic herbs, turned on their master and tore him to pieces. And when the throne passed to Bellerophon, son of Glaucus, he also tasted the bitterness of family misfortune, having to flee from Corinth when he accidentally killed a kinsman.

Bellerophon fled to his neighbour King Proetus, but the malice of Fate was not done with him yet. Anteia, wife of Proetus, fell in love with him and, when her passion was not returned, falsely accused him of trying to seduce her. Proetus believed his wife yet could not with honour kill a suppliant at his court. To settle the matter, he sent Bellerophon to Asia Minor, with a sealed letter for Anteia's father, requesting him to put an end to the bearer, 'for the sake of your daughter and my wife.'

Anteia's father, Iobates, felt no ill-will towards this royal stranger but he could not ignore a request from his son-in-law. Seeking a way to satisfy both Proetus and his own conscience, he sent Bellerophon on an impossible mission. This was to kill the Chimaera, a fire-breathing monster, daughter of Typhon, with a lion's head, the body of a goat and a tail that ended in a serpent's venomous head. To kill her was a hard and perilous task, and one which many men had perished to achieve. No ordinary horse could brave the monster's fiery breath and before Bellerophon set out, a seer advised him to catch and tame Pegasus, the winged horse which lived on the Muses' sacred mountain at Helicon. At first, Bellerophon found the horse too wild even to

touch: it rose disdainfully and swiftly into the air at the least approach. After many efforts, Bellerophon lay down to an exhausted sleep; as he slept, he dreamed that Athene appeared and showed him a bridle that would tame the horse. And when he awoke a golden bridle lay beside him on the grass. Pegasus was standing warily nearby, ready to fly if any danger threatened. Cautiously, Bellerophon approached, and threw the bridle over the horse's tossing head. At once Pegasus was still and manageable.

Pegasus carried Bellerophon through the air to the Chimaera's lair. Then, as the horse wheeled and pranced above it, beyond the reach of its snarling jaws and serpent's tail, Bellerophon fired volleys of arrows down until the beast lay dead.

Iobates welcomed Bellerophon home and praised his courage, but secretly he still plotted to kill him. He sent Bellerophon to fight all the enemies of his kingdom, certain that somewhere he would surely fall in battle. First, he attacked the Solymoi, then the warlike Amazons, and then he cleared the bandits from the Lycian plain. And every time Bellerophon returned triumphant and unharmed. At last Iobates was ashamed, for he realized that

this hero was no ordinary mortal but one favoured with greatness by the gods. He learned from Bellerophon the real account of what had happened with Anteia, and as an act of repentance he gave him half his kingdom and his second daughter in marriage.

For a long while Bellerophon prospered in Lycia. Then fortune turned full circle once again. Pride and presumption brought his downfall for he tried to ride the winged Pegasus up to heaven. Zeus struck him from the horse's back and he fell back to earth, a broken man. Bellerophon's son was killed in war and his daughter shot by one of Artemis' arrows. Lamed, lonely and finally cursed by the gods, Bellerophon wandered on the Aleian plain, far from all human life, until Death led him away to the Underworld.

## Mythical beasts

The Chimaera was one of many nightmare creatures which combined several of the more alarming features, such as beaks, tusks, horns, claws and fangs, with which the animal world attacks its prey or defends itself against man. The Mesopotamian monarchs had adorned their palaces with creatures like these to symbolize their own power and ferocity. For the Greeks they belonged to the world of far away or long ago, useful and picturesque subjects for sculpture or vase-painting or as bogeys to scare children into good behaviour.

Pegasus was alone among these composite creatures in being at all amiable, and even Pegasus was a difficult and dangerous mount to handle. The idea of galloping among the clouds seems still to have a powerful appeal despite the familiarity of air travel.

The most famous mythical beast was the Sphinx, whose riddle was solved by Oedipus. It had a female face, a lion's body, and eagle's wings. The idea of a sphinx probably came, via Syria, from Egypt where sphinxes were shown with a male face, a lion's body and no wings. They are thought to have represented the rising sun.

# The family of horror

Sad land of Argos, around your bloodstained walls a history of tragedy repeated itself from generation to generation! Strangers came with guilty hands. Cries of hatred and violence echoed among the dry fields and in the sun-baked streets of your cities.

First, restless Pelops, son of Tantalus whom the gods detested, came from the Asian shore to seek a new home across the Aegean. Hearing that King Oenomaus of Pisa had a daughter of great beauty, Pelops wooed her and won her love. But Oenomaus had devised a strange contest for her hand. He challenged each suitor to a chariot race. The prize to be won was his daughter Hippodameia, and the penalty for the loser was death. Twelve suitors had already run the course, and twelve heads lined the palace gate at Pisa.

Such brutal blood-lust was offensive to the gods, so when Pelops prayed to Poseidon for help, the Earth-Shaker, who was also god of horses, sent him a golden chariot drawn by winged horses. Still Pelops was unsure of his success, for the horses of Oenomaus were born of the wind and able to outrun even the swift horses of the gods. He therefore took aside Myrtilus, the king's charioteer, and promised him the first rites of Hippodameia's wedding night, if he would betray his master. Myrtilus agreed, for he too loved Hippodameia, and he replaced the linch-pins on the axles of the king's chariot with wax.

Both teams set off furiously towards the Isthmus of Corinth. Neck and neck they raced but soon Oenomaus began to gain on his rival. Then the wax melted under the friction of the axle, the wheels flew off, and Oenomaus was dragged to death in his wrecked chariot. Pelops claimed Hippodameia, but instead of giving Myrtilus the agreed reward, he flung the charioteer into the sea. As the waves closed over him, Myrtilus cursed Pelops and his house forever.

At first, this curse seemed unanswered by the gods. Pelops married Hippodameia, sent his armies out from Pisa in Elis and conquered most of the territory below the Isthmus of Corinth. The country he had won he renamed the Peloponnese, after himself, and eventually ruled this wide realm from the old city of Argos. In time, he was blessed with many children, among whom were two sons, Atreus and Thyestes.

From their earliest years these two were headstrong rivals in most things but in particular for the kingship of Mycenae. When Atreus took a wife, Aerope, his brother's rivalry intruded even here, for Thyestes won Aerope's heart and they became secret lovers. Together they plotted to make Thyestes king, using Atreus' own deception to gain their ends. That season, Atreus had made a promise to the goddess Artemis that he would sacrifice to her the finest animal in his flock. But when one of his ewes gave birth to a golden lamb, he could not bear to part with its wonderful fleece, which he regarded as an emblem of kingship. He gave the lamb's flesh as a burnt offering but locked the precious fleece inside a chest. That night, Aerope opened the chest, removed the fleece and gave it to her lover. Later, when the question of the kingship was debated, Thyestes cunningly suggested that he who had the fleece should be king. Atreus confidently agreed, whereupon

## Chariots and chariot racing

In chariot warfare massed chariots were used much as squadrons of cavalry were subsequently used, to break up formations of infantry and to pursue and cut to pieces an army in flight. The advantage the charioteer had over the cavalryman was that in times when stirrups were unknown a chariot provided a better platform from which to shoot arrows or hurl spears than the back of a horse. Eventually the comparative disadvantages, such as unsuitability for rough terrain and inferior mobility, made chariots obsolete in warfare. By Homer's time, battles were fought by infantry and cavalry, but his knowledge of the traditions told him that the heroes of the Mycenaean Age had fought from chariots. The traditions, however, did not tell him how the chariots had been used, so in the *Iliad* they are little more than a convenient means of transport to and from the midst of the battle. Though obsolete in warfare chariots continued to be used for sport for another thousand years at least. Chariot racing was included in the Olympian games from early in the seventh century BC, and a chariot victory brought immense prestige to the man who had trained and entered the team (which was driven by a professional charioteer). Only kings, tyrants or very wealthy citizens could afford to race chariots.

The Olympian games, like all the athletic contests of the Greeks, were part of a religious festival. The festival was dedicated to Zeus and the most impressive building—among many impressive buildings—in the sacred precinct where the religious ceremonies took place was the temple of Zeus. It was built in the middle of the fifth century BC and contained carvings by the finest sculptors living at the time. On the east pediment was carved the scene before the race in which Pelops won Hippodameia and Oenomaus was killed. Between the two teams with their charioteers and their grooms stands the figure of Zeus—the dispenser of justice and the guardian of oaths. Among the spectators is a prophet whose concerned expression shows that he foresees the result of the race—the death of Oenomaus and his charioteer by an act of treachery which led to so many crimes.

The festival of Olympia had been founded by the people of Pisa (the city of the legendary Oenomaus) and Oenomaus' legendary race had begun at Olympia, so this must have seemed a very suitable episode to display so prominently in the sacred precinct, where it would be seen by the charioteers as they arrived for the festival with their teams of horses. There was an additional significance for all the athletes in the representation of a legend involving cheating and broken oaths and their consequences. Before the games began every competitor had to stand at the altar of Zeus and affirm on oath two things: that he had trained for at least ten months before the games and that he would never cheat in any of the contests he competed in.

Thyestes immediately produced the fleece, and won the kingdom.

Zeus, however, was not pleased with Thyestes' cheating ways and sent a curious message to Atreus: 'Challenge your brother to give up the kingdom if the sun can be made to run backwards.' Puzzled, but obedient to the great god's command, Atreus made the challenge and Thyestes accepted this ridiculous proposition with amusement. Then, as the midday sun blazed down on earth, Zeus ordered Helius to pull his team of horses around in mid-journey and return the fiery chariot of the sun to its eastern home. This sign from the heavens made Thyestes' wrong-doing plain, and he had no choice but to abandon the kingdom and go into exile.

Atreus ruled in Argos but still he could not forgive his brother, since he now learned for the first time that Thyestes was the lover of his wife. He pondered darkly on his revenge. When his plan was complete he tempted his brother to return by offering a half-share of the kingdom; then he prepared a special feast to receive him. Tearing Thyestes' children from sanctuary, Atreus butchered them and served them in a stew to their unsuspecting father. When Thyestes had eaten his fill, the heads of his children were ceremonially brought in on silver plates, to demonstrate to all the world what a horrifying dish he had eaten.

Sick with disgust and despair, Thyestes called the gods to witness, cursed Atreus and fled once more. At Sicyon, he consulted an oracle on the best way to gain revenge and was advised that only his child by his own daughter would avenge him. The word of the oracle was a matter of dread to him, but his hatred of his brother was now so extreme that he ravished his remaining daughter, Pelopia, who in due course gave birth to a son; she named him Aegisthus.

Now the many curses called down on Pelops and his children began to take effect. Plague and famine stalked the countryside around Mycenae and in the lands of Argos. Atreus blamed Thyestes and, knowing that he could never be secure while his brother lived, sent his sons Agamemnon and Menelaus to capture him. They took their uncle by chance, on the way to Delphi, and threw him in prison, but their plan went disastrously awry. The young Aegisthus freed his father secretly then sent a blood-stained sword to Atreus as lying evidence of Thyestes' death. Fortified by a sacred oath of revenge, Aegisthus took that same sword in the night and killed King Atreus. His murdered brothers and sisters were avenged.

Victims became offenders. Vengeance passed from hand to hand. Families that had suffered took up the sword of the aggressor. Agamemnon, who had fled on the death of his father, returned to drive Thyestes and Aegisthus out of Mycenae and claim the kingdom for himself. Fate used him well and he became the greatest of the Argive princes.

Agamemnon married Clytaemnestra, the widow of a conquered king. Though Clytaemnestra bore him several children, her marriage with Agamemnon was far from happy. It had begun in violence and it continued in sullen resignation. So when Agamemnon received the call to lead the men of Argos to the Trojan War, his wife watched him go without regret. Soon she was to have further reasons for resentment.

The princes of Hellas gathered at Aulis under the general command of Agamemnon, and waited for a favourable wind to send the assembled ships to Troy. While Agamemnon passed the time hunting, he shot a deer at long range and boasted to his companions that not even Artemis could do better. Artemis, who was notoriously touchy for her honour, withheld the wind and the great fleet lay harmless and becalmed until Agamemnon made amends: prayers and burnt offerings were in vain. Nothing but the sacrifice of his daughter, Iphegenia, would satisfy the goddess.

By a trick, Clytaemnestra was persuaded to bring Iphigeneia to Aulis, where the maiden nobly offered her own life for the success of the expedition, and to her mother's grief was led to the altar. Some say that Artemis at the last moment substituted a hind or a she-bear and carried Iphigeneia off in a cloud to the land of the Taurians. But Clytaemnestra returned home with a bitter heart and set her mind implacably against her husband.

So when Aegisthus returned from exile, looking for revenge against his hated cousin, it was not hard for him to worm his way into the good graces of Clytaemnestra. Soon they were living together in adultery, plotting to keep the kingdom from Agamemnon, should he ever return from Troy. For ten years they waited, until news came that Agamemnon was sailing home victorious, bringing with him the Trojan princess Cassandra and their two children. The lovers in Mycenae resolved to kill them all.

The weary general landed and Clytaemnestra took him by the hand, to wipe away the stain of travel in the aromatic waters of the bath-house. At the palace door Cassandra stopped in a trance. She would go no further, for she sniffed the stench of blood. Agamemnon entered and bathed, but as he stepped naked from the water his enemies confronted him. Clytaemnestra covered him with a net, Aegisthus gave two terrible blows, and Clytaemnestra completed the murder by striking off her husband's head. Without waiting to close his eyes, she rushed outside and took the life of Cassandra with one swing of her murderous axe. Then the soldiers of Aegisthus fell upon the men of Agamemnon's guard, and the dead bodies dropped between the long tables set for the homecoming feast. With surprise on his side, Aegisthus won the day, consigning to the Underworld, as his last victims, the two little sons of Cassandra. Then the gory sword returned to the scabbard.

When the deed was done, once again the young took up the duty imposed on them by the blood and fury of their fathers. Agamemnon's son, Orestes, was saved by his nurse from Aegisthus' sword and knew that the time must come when he would avenge his father. He grew up safe in the shadow of Mount Parnassus, away from his accursed homeland. But when he was fully grown, the Delphic oracles recalled him to his filial duty. Secretly, he travelled to Mycenae, to pour libations and offer a lock of hair at his father's tomb. His

## The murder of Agamemnon

When Odysseus, in the *Odyssey*, visited the House of Hades and talked with the dead he was surprised to find King Agamemnon there, having last seen him setting sail for home after the sack of Troy. Agamemnon explains that on his return to Mycenae he had been invited to a banquet by Aegisthus and Clytaemnestra and then murdered with all his comrades. Most pitiful of all, Agamemnon said, was the cry of Priam's daughter Cassandra whom treacherous Clytaemnestra slew beside him.

From this story the playwright, Aeschylus (who claimed to be giving to his audiences 'helpings from the banquet of Homer') made one of the most powerful and unforgettable tragedies ever written. He simplified and concentrated the story by having Clytaemnestra kill her husband Agamemnon herself, single-handed, in long-meditated revenge for her beloved daughter Iphigeneia, whom Agamemnon had callously sacrificed for the sake of fair winds for his fleet. On his arrival at the palace she deceives him with a pretence of loving joy, and entices him with a purple carpet to betray his arrogant vanity as he enters the palace. There, out of sight of the audience, when she is presumed to be washing her husband's travel-stained limbs in preparation for a thanksgiving sacrifice, a horrifying cry is heard. He is being struck three deadly blows with an axe as he struggles in the folds of an all-enveloping robe she has prepared for him. In Aeschylus' play there is no banquet and there are no comrades present, only Cassandra whom Clytaemnestra slaughters beside him. It is not until the two bodies have been brought out of the palace with an exulting Clytaemnestra beside them that Aegisthus appears, a cowardly fellow-conspirator, bringing a bodyguard to cow the outraged citizens.

Audiences have been thrilled or shocked by the enactment of murders in innumerable plays since the time of Aeschylus and no one would suppose that the spectacle of an exulting wife who has just murdered her husband and his mistress is of itself a spiritual experience. What is so profoundly moving

*Continued over page*

in this play is that Clytaemnestra, standing, bloody axe in hand beside the bodies, does not realize what she has done—but the audience does. She believes that she has just accomplished, against the odds, a predestined act of revenge for which she has incurred no guilt. The audience, having heard all that has been said while she was off stage, sense the ancient goddesses of revenge; they have been haunting the family of Agamemnon for three generations already, and are now waiting to exact vengeance for yet another, even more horrifying deed—Clytemnaestra's own murder by her son, Orestes.

In just under 1700 lines Aeschylus has evoked, as a background to the murders, the sufferings of war inflicted on the innocent. The audience have been reminded of the hardships endured by fighting men—the anxieties of families waiting at home for their loved ones who may well be returned to them as an urnful of ashes; the tragedy of the women in the smoking ruins of the conquered city as they lament over the bodies of their menfolk, and resign themselves to a life of slavery.

Aeschylus himself had fought in two battles against the Persians. He had seen his own city twice sacked by them and knew the fate of other cities they had captured—in particular Miletus, where the men were all killed and the women and children sold into slavery.

The poets who competed in the Festival were required to put on three tragedies and a satyr play (a kind of comic play involving satyrs). The three tragedies did not have to be on the same theme, but the murder of Agamemnon left the audience knowing that there must be a sequel—the murder of Clytemnestra. This sequel ended with the appearance of the Furies, age-old goddesses of retribution, who came to hound Orestes to madness and destruction. Aeschylus' third tragedy showed a jury trial and the spirit of wise compromise laying to rest the curse of Agamemnon's family. Justice was accomplished without giving cause for further bloodshed thanks to the political machinery of the recently established Athenian democracy.

sister, Electra, coming later to make her own offering, sensed his presence and joyfully welcomed her long-absent brother. Together they planned the downfall of their mother and her lover.

While her children were conspiring against her, Clytaemnestra was tormented in her sleep, dreaming that she had given birth to a serpent, which sucked at her breast. Surely, Orestes was that serpent. When his plans were ready, he knocked at the palace gate, pretending to be a strange messenger bringing news of his own death. And this news seemed to be confirmed when, to Clytaemnestra's joy, a second messenger arrived with an urn said to contain Orestes' ashes. Clytaemnestra and Aegisthus came in person to welcome these strange bearers of good news. Then Orestes, his sword grimly upheld, made himself known to them. Without compunction, as the voice of Apollo had ordered him at Delphi, he killed his mother and Aegisthus. Some say this happened at Mycenae, others at Argos. But all agree that Orestes displayed the bloodstained net that had entrapped Agamemnon. Standing over the dead bodies, he called upon the gods to acknowledge the justice of his act, a fit reward for so treacherous and adulterous a pair.

Just though his cause might be, Orestes could not avoid the primeval punishment for matricide. The age-old Furies hunted him down and Orestes fled before them. For a year he fled as they pursued, half-crazy from the agony of their tortures. And the black deities of vengeance did not release him until Olympian Apollo, at whose orders the crime had been committed, led Orestes to Athens, to judge his case once and for all before the court of the Areopagus. When the stones were cast, the vote was even. Then Athene, guardian of the city, threw her pebble on Orestes' side, and the grumbling Erinyes at last gave up the chase.

Blood enough had been spilt in the lands of Argos. The curse on Pelops and his children had run far enough, from generation to generation. The gods intervened and brought the cycle of vengeance to an end.

# THE LABOURS OF HERACLES

## The birth of a hero

There was a time when the kingdom of Mycenae faced many enemies. The king was always at war. He had eight sons to help him, but even that number seemed hardly enough. He hurried from danger to danger, marshalling his sons at this besieged town or sending them in counter-attack to that far place. Eventually, battered by the fortunes of war, he had no sons left. They had all died in battle. Anxious about the succession and needing allies to continue his wars, the king betrothed his daughter Alcmene to a neighbouring prince called Amphitryon. This prince was pleased to be chosen, for Alcmene was a beautiful maiden, but in an unlucky moment, aiming his club at some disorderly cattle, he killed the king by accident: Amphitryon and Alcmene fled to Thebes.

Although Alcmene forgave her husband, she did not forget her duty to her family and before she would consent to live with Amphitryon, she asked him to complete her father's campaign. While Amphitryon was away, chasing the old enemy with great success, Zeus saw that the beautiful Alcmene was alone. Ordering the sun god Helius to unhitch his horses and spend the day at home, Zeus took on the person of Amphitryon and came stealthily in the dark to Alcmene. Assuring her that her father's enemies were no more, he comforted her for a night which lasted as long as three. He had plans of glory for this mortal princess and her offspring, which were not to be achieved in a hurry. As Zeus left in the darkness before dawn, just as well-rested Helius was once more yoking his horses to the fiery chariot of the sun, Alcmene was surprised to find the real Amphitryon slipping in triumph into the conjugal bed, weary but anxious for the rewards of victory. As a result of this double visit, which neither Amphitryon nor his wife could explain, Alcmene conceived twin children.

Now Hera, Queen of Heaven, was particularly furious at this latest of Zeus' infidelities, for her divine knowledge told her that greatness was in store for Alcmene's son. She set her wits against the Father of the Gods and tried everything to frustrate his plan. Hera knew that another mortal child was about to be born into a family which also traced its bloodline back to Zeus. So she wrung from Zeus this oath: 'The child of my divine blood who is born before nightfall to a mortal woman, will be lord of all around him.'

Alcmene's child was ready to be born that day, but Hera sent Eileithyia, goddess of childbirth, to sit before her with crossed legs and so delay the birth. To complete her plan, the infant Eurystheus, descended from Perseus, Zeus and Danaë's son, was brought prematurely into the world at Tiryns. Thus Eurystheus claimed the benefit of Zeus' oath and became lord of all Argos.

Alcmene gave birth to twins, Heracles and Iphicles, and to begin with it was a puzzle to say which was the son of a god and which the son of a human. The doubt was resolved when the children were a few months old and Hera sent two serpents to attack the babes in the cradle. Iphicles howled with terror, but little Heracles, without a whimper, took a serpent in each hand and strangled them.

As Heracles grew, only the greatest of teachers were good enough for a child with his divine blood. A grandson of Apollo taught him archery, the trickster Autolycus showed him the inner secrets of wrestling, and Polydeuces, most famous of swordsmen, was his sword-master. Linus, a son of Apollo, taught him music, but Heracles was not much interested in the soft arts of peace. When Linus beat his pupil to correct him, Heracles

battered his master with the lyre so badly that
Linus died. Heracles avoided punishment by
pleading self-defence, but Amphitryon now found
it safer to send him out with the flocks and the
herds. Country living suited him. His eyes flashed
fire, he could eat a whole ox at a sitting, his arrows
never missed, and his spear split tree-trunks.

When he was eighteen, and returning from a
successful lion-hunt on Mount Cithaeron, Heracles
met heralds coming from the Minyans to demand
tribute from Thebes. Heracles cut off their noses
and ears, tied these around their necks, and sent
them packing back to their master. This provoked
war, but Heracles, armed by Athene, led the
Thebans to an easy victory and won from the
Minyans a tribute twice as valuable as the one they
had themselves hoped to collect. After this victory,
King Creon of Thebes gave Heracles his daughter
Megara in marriage.

For some years Heracles lived in Thebes,
winning a reputation as a fearsome warrior and
raising several children. News of his fame reached
Hera and re-awakened her old angry resentment so
that she sent him a madness which caused him to
kill his whole family; his wife, his children and
even some of the children of his brother, Iphicles,
were destroyed, some shot with arrows, others
stabbed and others set on fire. When Heracles
came to his senses and knew what he had done, he
fled in despair, going first to neighbouring King
Thespius for ritual purification, and then, humbly,
to Delphi to learn his penance. The priestess
banished him to Tiryns: 'There you shall live for
twelve years, in servitude to King Eurystheus,
subject to his least command. When that is done
you will become immortal.'

With heavy heart, Heracles turned south for
Tiryns, with his nephew and young friend Iolaus as
charioteer and shield-bearer. Hera had set herself
grimly against him, but as a favourite son of Zeus he
had the help of other gods. Athene smiled on him
and gave him his travel-cloak. Hephaestus forged
him a bronze breast-plate, Hermes gave him a
sword, and Apollo provided the mighty bow and
the unerring arrows.

## The twelve labours

Eurystheus was a mean-spirited king. With the help of Hera's trickery, he had already stolen the birthright of Heracles. Now he searched for the most hazardous tasks to test his heroic but reluctant servant.

The first labour which he imposed upon Heracles was to kill and skin the lion of Nemea. This huge beast, an offspring of the monstrous Typhon, was so hungry for prey that it had almost emptied the land of victims, leaving the countryside under an eerie silence. It lived in a blood-spattered cave with two entrances, and it feared nothing, for no weapon could penetrate its skin.

Following the trail of the lion into the desolate hills, where even the birds did not sing, Heracles was puzzled how to overcome it. When he had tracked it to its lair, he loosed a flight of arrows, but these had no more effect on the beast than drops of rain. Nor did his sword-thrusts make any mark on the invulnerable skin. So he battered the lion with his mighty club of seasoned olive-wood until it retreated, annoyed but unhurt, into its den. Since no sword nor arrows nor club could harm it, Heracles determined to tackle it with bare hands. He stopped up one entrance to the cave, advanced into the other, wrestled the lion into an arm-lock and, with superhuman strength, choked it to death. To skin a pelt which no knife could cut would have been a problem to a lesser man but Heracles had an inspiration and used the animal's own razor-sharp claws. He flayed it and dressed it, and forever afterwards wore it as his own distinctive cloak. The great snarling skull covered his head like a helmet, and the impenetrable skin kept him safe from all weapons.

Heracles strode back to Tiryns with the lion-skin around his shoulders and the sight of the lion-clad figure marching towards the city so frightened Eurystheus that he shut the gates and forbade Heracles to step beyond the walls. In future, if the king had anything to say to the hero he would send a herald. And for even greater safety,

Eurystheus had a large bronze jar buried in the ground, in which he planned to hide whenever Heracles returned from his labours with another terrifying specimen.

For the second labour, Eurystheus sent Heracles to kill the Hydra which lived in the swamps of Lerna. This monster, another evil child of Typhon, had a bloated, dog-like body and nine snaky heads which gushed forth poisonous breath. The heads snatched in every direction, tangling victims in the long coiling necks, hissing and spitting venom.

Heracles drove the beast from the deep swamp, where a man could get no footing, by showering it with burning arrows. Then he set about it with his formidable club. But as each head was struck off, a new one took its place, more furious, more venomous than the last. To confuse him further, Hera sent a giant crab to attack Heracles from the rear and clamp him in its claws. While Heracles was stamping on the crab, crushing its shell, he shouted to his charioteer Iolaus to take a flaming torch and with it burn the Hydra's necks as each head fell, so that a new one could not grow. At last only the Hydra's one immortal head remained and this one Heracles cut off with a golden sickle and buried, still hissing, deep in the ground. He then butchered the body and took the Hydra's gall in which to dip his arrows. In future, the slightest scratch from one of these meant certain death.

When Heracles returned, Eurystheus, peering from his bronze hide-away, received the news of the Hydra's death with criticism rather than praise. Since Iolaus had helped with the task, this did not count as a true labour, he said. Heracles would have to do better if Eurystheus was to release him from his bondage.

Next, Heracles was sent to capture the hind of Ceryneia. This graceful deer, with bronze hooves and golden antlers, was sacred to Artemis, the goddess of hunting, and therefore must not be killed. The only hope of taking it unhurt was to try to run it down, but since the animal was as swift as the wind it led Heracles a weary chase. For a year he followed it, up and down the Peloponnese and even (some say) as far afield as the frozen lands of the Hyperboreans. At last, he surprised it as it slept, exhausted, on the bank of the River Ladon.

Heracles gathered the feet of the deer in his powerful hands, heaved the struggling animal across his back, and set out for Argos. But the twin gods Artemis and Apollo met him on the way, and Artemis sternly demanded what he was doing with her sacred property. By a piece of quick thinking, Heracles laid the blame on Eurystheus and the goddess allowed him to go on his way, on condition that the hind was freed at the end of his journey.

The fourth labour, the pursuit and live capture of the Erymanthian boar, involved Heracles in some unfortunate accidents. On the way to the hunt, Heracles stopped and rested at the home of the Centaur Pholus. For this important guest, the Centaur served a feast—raw meat for himself and roasted meat for Heracles. However, he was reluctant to open any of his flagons of wine, for the Centaurs owned all their wine in common and, he claimed, it was not his to give. After many hours of travelling, Heracles was thirsty and he finally persuaded Pholus to produce the wine. But as soon as the other Centaurs sniffed it, they made an angry attack. While Pholus hid, Heracles drove the Centaurs back, killing some and causing others to flee to their king, Cheiron. Heracles pursued them to the very threshhold of their refuge, firing his arrows as he ran.

Unhappily, the last arrow by chance hit wise old Cheiron in the knee. The wound itself was not a serious one but the Hydra's poison on the arrow tip made it deadly. Heracles himself dressed the wound, but Cheiron could not escape the pain. And because he was immortal, he could not even find relief in death. At last, so great was his agony, that he gave away his immortality and chose voluntarily to die.

Returning to the Centaurs' cave, Heracles came upon another accident. When Pholus came out of hiding and began to bury his dead comrades, he slipped as he was removing one of Heracles' arrows from a Centaur's body and the tip pierced his foot, killing him instantly with its poison.

Heracles buried his friend Pholus with full honours and then hurried away from that unlucky country.

Heracles now took up the trail of the boar and drove it higher and higher along the ridges of Erymanthus. Among the snows of the tallest peaks, the boar blundered into a deep drift, enabling Heracles to leap upon its back and bind it fast. With the great beast struggling on his shoulders, Heracles returned to Eurystheus. But the king took one look at the boar, with its massive quivering body and its tusks like scythes and its grizzly outraged snout, and jumped straight back into his bronze jar.

For the fifth labour, Eurystheus was able to present Heracles with a particularly unpleasant task. Augeias, King of Elis, had the largest flocks and herds of all mankind. His animals were fertile and healthy so that their numbers multiplied amazingly. But since the king never bothered to clean out the sheep-folds and the stables and the cattle-yards, the dung was piled up to the eaves and overflowed the fields, so that they were neither ploughed nor sown. The heaps of manure stank out the land and raised a pestilence right across the Peloponnese. Eurystheus ordered Heracles to clean away all this filth.

When he had surveyed the task, Heracles offered to complete it in one day. Augeias was amused. Tauntingly, he offered the hero one tenth of his flocks if the work was done by nightfall, and both men sealed the bargain with oaths. Then Heracles set to. He breached the walls of the stables and the pens, and he diverted the rivers Alpheus and Peneius to flow through the gaps he had made. The waters roared through the yards and down the valleys until the ground was scoured clean of the dung. By nightfall it was all gone and the air was sweet for the first time that men could remember.

When Heracles came to claim his reward, Augeias refused to pay him, on the grounds that Heracles had acted merely as the servant of Eurystheus. And when the matter was taken to arbitration, Augeias flew into a rage and banished Heracles from Elis, saying that his achievement was only a trick and that it was the two river gods who had done the real work. So Heracles returned to Tiryns empty-handed, only to face the familiar complaints of Eurystheus. Once again, he rejected Heracles' labour, because it had been performed in the hope of a reward and was therefore not an act of servitude.

In the wilds of Arcadia, among the dense woods that lined the borders of the lake at Stymphalus, there lived an almost countless flock of man-eating birds. The destruction of these birds was the sixth labour given to Heracles.

The birds were not very large — about the size of a heron — but they dived on their prey in great masses, and each was able to pierce a metal breast-plate with its strong beak. At first, Heracles wondered how to attack them. They were hidden in the forest and his arrows were useless in the thick brush. But Athene came to his aid. She brought him a pair of brazen cymbals and told him to stand on a mound overlooking the lake and to clash the cymbals with all his might. As he did so, a vast cloud of birds rose in alarm and Heracles shot them down as fast as he could draw his bow. Those that escaped the massacre spiralled into the upper air and fled in panic, never to return.

After so successfully conquering the beasts and monsters of the Peloponnese, Heracles was now sent further afield. For the seventh labour, Eurystheus sent him to fetch a bull from Crete.

Bulls were forever famous in the island of Crete and whether this was the bull whose form Zeus took to steal Europa, or the one which Poseidon sent later from the sea, the tellers of this tale do not divulge. But they relate how, after wrestling the bull for a long time, Heracles mastered it, rode it across the sea, and drove it to Mycenae — where Eurystheus promptly released it. Some say he dedicated it to Hera but the goddess would have nothing to do with a beast provided by Heracles. Others say the king simply let the bull go. This was unfortunate, for the animal, which was powerful and hungry, went marauding all the way to the plains of Marathon where, to prevent further damage, Theseus caught it and sacrificed it to Athene.

From the island of Crete, Heracles was sent next to the northern mountains of Thrace, where his eighth labour was to catch and subdue the mares of Diomedes.

This Diomedes, a son of Ares and king of the treacherous Bistones, was as wild and cruel as his own landscape and his horses were of the same temper. They fed on human flesh and the king liked to fill their mangers with the bodies of his enemies. Sailing for Thrace with a band of helpers, Heracles took the grooms by surprise and had the horses out of the stable before the guards were aroused. Diomedes and his men followed in hot pursuit and, to free himself for the fight, Heracles left the horses in the charge of his friend Abderus. In the battle, the king's men were routed. Heracles himself stunned Diomedes with his club. As he dragged the king towards the place where he had left the horses, he found to his dismay that they had killed and devoured poor Abderus. Heracles buried his friend with full rites, and by the tomb, the city of Abdera was later founded. As for Diomedes, Heracles threw him to his own horses in disgust.

With much trouble, Heracles drove the mares to Argolis, but again Eurystheus mocked Heracles' achievement and set them free. Unused to the southern country, the horses became lost in the mountains where they were soon destroyed by lions and other savage beasts.

For the ninth labour, Eurystheus sent Heracles to the Black Sea, to claim a golden girdle from the Amazon Queen Hippolyte.

The Amazons were warrior-women descended from Ares. Their society and their lives were dedicated to war, so much so that they cut off the right breast in order to draw the bow more easily. Their men, poor menial beings, were crippled at birth so that they would not stray far from household work. But the women were practised soldiers and Heracles took a strong company of men to face them. The long sea-voyage from Argolis brought many adventures and their ships were blown from one landfall to another. When eventually they arrived at the Amazon port of

Themiscyra, on the Black Sea, Heracles was surprised to find Hippolyte waiting quite peacefully to meet him.

The queen was intent on a contest of another kind, for she was won over by Heracles' reputation and infatuated by his powerful body and his noble presence. She was ready to offer him the golden girdle as a token of love. However, Hera was displeased that things should go so easily for her enemy, and spread a rumour among the Amazons that this foreign hero was about to abduct their queen. The angry women responded with an attack on the ships. Heracles suspected that Hippolyte herself had laid the plot. Without asking questions, he seized her, killed her, took the girdle and cast off from the furious women as fast as possible.

On the way back from the Black Sea, landing at Troy for rest and supplies, Heracles found the city in deep distress, suffering the pains of divine displeasure. Some years before, Poseidon and Apollo had protected Troy with a great wall, but King Laomedon had refused them their reward. Very soon the king learned that it was not wise to break one's word and doubly foolish to try to cheat the gods. Apollo sent a plague and Poseidon a sea-monster to destroy the city and its people. In time, a penitent Laomedon acknowledged his sin and, just as Heracles arrived, the king was leading out his daughter Hesione as a sacrificial offering to the sea-monster.

Heracles, to whom any monster was a challenge, bargained with Laomedon. He would save the girl if Laomedon would give him some horses which Zeus had presented to the city. When the king agreed, Heracles leaped down the monster's open throat and killed it from within its belly. But Laomedon once again went back on his word and withheld the reward. In a hurry to be home and anxious to give Hippolyte's girdle to Eurystheus, Heracles did not take instant revenge. Instead he cursed the king and warned him that in years to come a terrible retribution would fall on Troy.

For the tenth labour, Heracles went to the western limit of the world, to fetch the red cattle of Geryon from the island of Erytheia. Geryon himself was fearful, a creature with three separate heads and bodies. His cattle, tended by a herdsman, were guarded by a watch-dog, Orthrus, brother to the hell-hound Cerberus. Undeterred, Heracles set out towards the far distant stream of Oceanus, where the island lay. Near the end of his journey, he came to the narrow strait where Asia and Europe nearly touched. To make the passage safer, he forced the continents apart, marking the points of the land with two great rocks, called, after him, the Pillars of Heracles. As he strained to push the lands apart, Helius beamed down on him with such heat that Heracles, sweating with exertion, threatened the sun god with his bow. This heroic but impossible gesture by a mere mortal so amused Helius that he gave Heracles a golden bowl in which to sail across Oceanus to the island of Erytheia.

When Heracles landed, the herdsman and the dog Orthrus rushed to attack, but Heracles struck them down with his club. Geryon, however, the grandson of a Titan, was a much more dangerous opponent and was not overcome until Heracles managed to pass an arrow through all three of his bodies. Then Heracles loaded the famous red cattle into Helius' bowl and sailed back to the shores of Europe, ready for the long, long cattle drive to the land of Argolis.

The return journey was troublesome and dangerous. The herd was tiresome to drive and difficult to keep together, and many robbers were waiting to pick off wandering cattle. In the Ligurian Alps, the Ligyes stole animals so persistently that Heracles wasted all his arrows holding them off. He prayed to Zeus for help and the Thunderer directed his path into a wasteland of stones where there was enough ammunition to beat away the plunderers. At Rhegium in southern Italy, a bull broke free and swam to Sicily where it mingled with the king's herd. When the king refused to return the animal, Heracles seized him in a wrestling hold and threw him to his death. From the foot of Italy, Heracles pressed on northwards and then across wild country to Thrace. There, Hera sent plagues of gadflies which maddened many animals, sending them galloping to their deaths in the wilderness.

After many months of travelling, and with the herd sadly diminished by the dangers of the road, Heracles had only a few cattle left when he reached the court of Eurystheus. The way had been long and hard, and it was made more dangerous by Hera's opposition. To try to appease the goddess, Heracles sacrificed the remaining cattle to his implacable foe.

Ten labours had taken eight years and one month, and Heracles had reason to hope that his work was nearly done. But Eurystheus had meanly discounted two of the labours and was casting about for further, more difficult trials to impose on his servant. For the eleventh labour, he ordered Heracles to go to the Garden of the Hesperides, to steal the Golden Apples which Mother Earth had given Hera as a wedding gift. These apples were guarded by the ever-watchful eyes of Ladon, the hundred-headed dragon who lay coiled around the foot of the apple tree.

As Heracles did not know where the Garden lay, he set out hopefully, questioning strangers, walking at random, wherever the path led him. In Macedonia, he would have killed a son of Ares in a duel had not Zeus parted them with a thunderbolt. Wandering further north, he fortunately came upon Nereus, the Old Man of the Sea, asleep on the cold banks of the Eridanus. Seizing the wise old man, and resolutely keeping hold while Nereus changed from one slippery shape to another, Heracles forced him to reveal where the Garden could be found.

The path was very long, leading again towards the misty western stream of Oceanus. Few knew the way, and Heracles wandered through many lands, seeking directions. The roads were often dangerous. In Libya, he was challenged by Antaeus, a giant son of Poseidon and Earth, who wrestled travellers, squeezing them to death. Each time Antaeus was thrown to the ground he gained extra strength, returning to the fight more powerful than before. Realizing this, Heracles held him aloft and did not put him down until the life was

crushed from him. Passing from Libya to Egypt, Heracles was captured by the soldiers of Busiris, another son of Poseidon. A seer had told Busiris that only the sacrifice of strangers could end an eight-year famine, so Heracles was bound and led to the altar. With the ritual axe of Busiris poised above him, Heracles burst his bonds and so escaped a fearful death. Still unsure of the way, Heracles left Africa and headed north once more, towards the unknown lands of the Hyperboreans. Following this road, he came to the crags in the Caucasus where Prometheus was chained in agony. After praying to Zeus for guidance, Heracles was permitted to release the long-suffering friend to mankind and to offer him the immortality which the poisoned Centaur Cheiron had voluntarily renounced.

At last, Heracles saw in the distance the towering figure of Atlas, bearing the sky on his shoulders. The golden fruit of the Hesperides shone in the Garden close by the giant's feet. Some say the task was now easy, that Heracles shot the dragon guardian with a poisoned arrow and picked the Golden Apples without more ado. But others claim that only Atlas could reach the fruit, and that Heracles took on the vast burden of the sky to free him for the task. When that was done, they say, Atlas rejoiced in his new-found freedom and declined to take back the sky. 'Well,' said Heracles, 'the least you can do is take over for a moment, while I make myself more comfortable.' The simple giant obeyed, and Heracles set off quickly with the apples, waving Atlas a cheerful goodbye. When Eurystheus had received the Golden Apples, the gods did not allow him to keep them. They were the divine property of Hera, too holy to remain in the possession of mankind. Athene collected them and carried them respectfully back to their proper place in the Garden of the Hesperides.

In the twelfth and last labour, Eurystheus hoped finally to defeat the superhuman strength and vitality of his servant. He set Heracles the most stupendous task of all: to overcome the forces of the Underworld and bring the watch-dog Cerberus from Tartarus.

Since this task was not to be undertaken lightly, Heracles went first to Eleusis, to be purified from the blood of the slaughtered Centaurs and to be initiated into the Mysteries of Demeter. Then, with Athene and Hermes to help him (without the gods, no man could return unscathed from this dark journey), Heracles entered the cave at Taenarum from where a short route descended to the realms of Tartarus.

In the strange darkness below, even Heracles felt menaced by unknown presences and needed the comforting hand of Athene. He thought he saw Medusa and drew his sword, but it was only a phantom. The shade of Meleager in bright armour made him start, but the sad spirit had only come to prophesy the hero's own end and to offer Heracles his sister Deianeira in marriage. Then Theseus and Peirithous called to him from the seat where Hades had bound them. He wrenched Theseus free, but abandoned Peirithous to eternal bondage. As he went deeper and deeper, and heard the moaning of the ghosts, Heracles pitied them and killed one of Hades' cattle so that they could drink the warm blood. The angry herdsman of the Underworld raged at his action and Heracles would have struck down the insolent fellow had not Persephone herself pleaded for the man.

In the black halls of deepest Tartarus, King Hades listened to Heracles' request. With grim humour he agreed to let Cerberus go, but only if Heracles could capture and manage the dog with his bare hands. Protected by his impenetrable lion-skin, Heracles grappled with the three-headed beast on the banks of the Acheron, subdued it, chained it and, assisted by Athene, dragged the fearsome hell-hound across the Styx and into the upper air by way of the cleft in the rocks at Troezen. Cerberus barked so long and loud at the bright sunlight that his saliva spread over the ground and brought forth poisonous aconites.

Triumphantly, Heracles returned to Eurystheus and presented the king with the monstrous, writhing bundle of fury. But Eurystheus was so frightened that he sent Cerberus straight back to Hades.

# Adventures and disaster

After all his years of servitude, Heracles had not changed. In fact, the twelve labours revealed his stormy character more clearly. He was overwhelmingly larger in scale than most ordinary humans could bear; lion-hearted, passionate, generous, an enemy to all tyrants, but also selfish, quick-tempered, brutal and careless of other lives. Heracles swept through the world like a tempest, and woe to anyone—man, woman, god or goddess—who stood in his way.

Impatient at lost years, Heracles returned to Thebes. Some say his wife Megara survived his murderous attack and waited for him there with love, but that he cast her casually aside. Soon he was wooing another wife, Iole, competing for her at archery. Though he won the contest, he was not given the prize and in his rage another fit of madness seized him. Accusing a friend of stealing cattle from him, he hurled the innocent man from the walls of Tiryns.

Stained once more with blood-guilt, Heracles looked again for purification but this time kings turned from him in disgust. Even the oracle at Delphi was so displeased with him that the priestess refused to answer his questions. Gripped by black fury, Heracles sacked the shrine, toppled the priestess from her sacred stool, and when Apollo hurried from Olympus to stop this impiety, Heracles grappled with the god himself until Zeus called a halt to the struggle with his thunderbolt. Even for a favourite son, Zeus could not overlook this outrage. Once more the gods sentenced the furious hero to a period of slavery.

With an eye for a bargain, Hermes, the god of commerce, hawked him around the courts of mankind. Omphale, Queen of Lydia, made the best offer and Heracles entered her service. Omphale was pleased to impose on her mighty servant some comic indignities, ordering him to wear women's clothes and do the housewife's tasks; but she allowed him also to work off his superhuman energy with bold exploits in many

lands. Once, returning to Omphale's court, Heracles awoke from a wayside nap to find the two Cercopes trying to steal his goods. These little men were notorious tricksters and a great trial to travellers. To teach them an uncomfortable lesson, Heracles hung them head-down from the ends of a pole and carried them away. Now, this unusual position gave them a good view of the hero's well-weathered backside, which his lordly lion-skin did not completely cover. They laughed so much at the undignified sight that Heracles stopped to discover the cause. Gasping for breath, they giggled out their explanation and Heracles, fortunately, saw the joke. Releasing the thieves from the pole, the three of them laughed so much that they could not walk, and sat down together on a rock to recover their breath. This rock, called the 'Black Bottom', is still shown in Thessaly.

For Heracles, the period spent with Omphale, far from being slavery, was a pleasant interlude, and he repaid the easy-going queen by defeating many of her enemies. But when Omphale released him, he still had serious matters of his own to attend to. He had sworn revenge on Laomedon of Troy, for breaking a promise, and he had a similar quarrel with Augeias of Elis, who had never paid his debt for the cleansing of his stables. His revenge for their bad faith was inevitable and severe. Troy and Elis were conquered, both kings killed and their kingdoms given away to others.

After some years of strenuous warfare, Heracles turned his thoughts once more to the softer joys of love and began to woo Deianeira, the woman promised to him in the Underworld. On the way home, Heracles and his bride came to the River Evenus in full spate. Deianeira hesitated at the roaring water, so the Centaur Nessus, claiming to be the ferryman, offered to carry her on his back. Heracles plunged ahead to the farther bank, but then, hearing the cries of his wife, he turned to see Nessus galloping off with her. Heracles drew his bow. His aim was perfect and the Centaur fell, mortally wounded. Before he died, the Centaur whispered instructions to Deianeira. She must take some of his blood, he said, and use it as a love-potion if Heracles ever grew tired of her. Its effect would be infallible.

That unhappy time came at last, and it happened in this way. Heracles, away from home to settle one more score, sent for his ceremonial robes so that his latest triumph could be celebrated in proper style. But Deianeira was full of fears. She heard that Heracles had killed the man who, long ago, had been his rival for the girl Iole. Now he was bringing Iole back with him in captivity. What did this mean? Was not Iole an old love? Was Heracles ready to abandon Deianeira for Iole? Remembering the dying Centaur's words, Deianeira decided to try the love-potion and smeared it on the ceremonial robes before sending them to her husband. When Heracles put on the robes, the terrible truth came out: the Centaur's blood was his revenge, no love-potion but a strong, corrosive poison which burned and could not be removed. Heracles, in agonized rage, knew his end was near. With skin on fire and blood boiling, he ordered his friends to carry him to Mount Oeta in Trachis, to prepare for death. Deianeira, aghast at what she had done, took her own life.

Between gasps of pain Heracles summoned his son: 'Swear by Zeus that you will take me to the highest peak and there burn me, without tears, on a pyre of oak and olive.' The preparations were soon made; the hero wearily climbed the pyre and sank down on his lion-skin. Still Heracles could not die, for no-one had the courage to light the deadly flame. At last a passing shepherd, bribed with the gift of Heracles' bow and arrows, set the torch to the wood. Flames flickered into life and leaped upwards through the small twigs, snapping and crackling through the dry kindling. But before they reached the hero's body, lying impatiently on the well-built pyre, a flash of lightning darted from the heavens. Great Zeus destroyed the mortal part of his favourite son and carried his immortal spirit to Olympus in a cloud.

With the acclaim of all the gods (even jealous Hera gave her reluctant assent), Heracles was deified and took his honoured place in the assembly of the mighty Olympians.

## Heracles and hero-worship

The Olympian gods had, in Greek mythology, either Cronus or Zeus for a father, and a goddess for their mother. The sons of Zeus (and of other gods) by mortal women were not immortal gods but mortal heroes. There were two exceptions: Dionysus and Heracles.

Dionysus, son of Zeus and Semele (the daughter of Cadmus, King of Thebes) was a special case. He was not born from Semele's womb but from the thigh of Zeus, and he was gifted with Divine powers—as heroes in their lifetime were not. Even so it was late in his career before he was received into the Divine family on Mount Olympus.

Heracles, son of Zeus and Alcmene (who was a grandchild of Perseus) was a true hero, like Theseus, or Agamemnon or Achilles. He had no divine powers during his lifetime, only extraordinary strength, courage and endurance. Nevertheless, unlike the other Greek heroes, he was, from the sixth century B C, believed to have earned immortality and a place among the gods by his sufferings and exertions on behalf of humanity. This conclusion to his career was not part of his myth as known to Homer and Hesiod. According to them he died and went down to Hades like any other hero; but for reasons as yet unexplained he came to be regarded as a god, and some verses of Homer and Hesiod were tampered with to make it appear that they, too, had said that he became, after his death, a god.

To Homer, and to the Ionian aristocrats among whom he lived, dead heroes were like any other dead—strengthless spirits incapable of helping or harming living people.

In mainland Greece throughout the Dark Ages, countrymen could see here and there in the depopulated countryside the burial mounds of once powerful Mycenaean princes —the Homeric heroes. These relics of a prosperous past must have acquired in the Dark Ages an aura of awe and sanctity for those who dwelt nearby. So it came to be felt that the heroes who had exercised so much power when alive on their own behalf, might now exercise it on behalf of the humble folk who came to pay to them tributes of sacrifices and offerings. Who better to give fertility to the earth and protection to the flocks, than a local spirit who would not be distracted, as Olympian gods might be, by the sacrifices and the prayers of the rich and the mighty in the great cities of the Greek world?

Sacrifices to the spirits of dead heroes (and to the gods of the Underworld) were different from the sacrifices made to the Olympians and other gods of the upper world. A black animal, often a ram, was the victim. The sacrifice took place at a lowly altar or beside a trench so that the blood of the victims would flow into the ground; and the victim's head was held down to symbolize that it was being killed for someone beneath the earth. In simpler sacrifices wine or olive oil or honey was poured into the earth.

Heracles was unique in that he received sacrifices both as god and hero—sacrifices of both black and white victims, on a high altar as well as on a low one or into a trench. He was, by the fifth century B C, one of the most widely invoked of gods or heroes, seeming more human and approachable than the awe-inspiring Olympians. His approachableness was enhanced by his reputation for human weaknesses, notably for over-indulgence in food, drink and sex.

There was a story about Heracles told (and perhaps invented) by one of those contemporaries of Socrates who claimed to teach wisdom for a fee (and who was despised for this by Socrates who thought that wisdom should be given freely). The story was that early in his life, 'at the time when young men become independent and show whether they are going to take the path of virtue or vice', Heracles was at a loss which path to take. As he sat wondering he was confronted by two fine-looking women, one handsome and modestly dressed, the other glamorous and seductive. Each, with persuasive arguments, offered to be his friend and guide, the one along the road of soft pleasures, the other along the stony road which led to honour and happiness through hardship, strife and working for the welfare of others. Heracles naturally, being such as he was, chose Arete (Virtue) for his friend and guide.

# THE VOYAGE OF THE ARGONAUTS

## The Golden Fleece

There was trouble in the palace of King Athamas of Boeotia. He was married to Nephele, whose name means 'cloud' and, though some say she was herself no more than a phantom created by Zeus, she bore the king two children, Phrixus and Helle. Then Athamas set her aside, married another woman, Ino, and made her queen in Nephele's place. The new queen hated her step-children, who still held their place in the king's heart, and she plotted to get rid of these rivals. She knew that Athamas would seek advice from Delphi if any misfortune fell upon the kingdom, so she persuaded the women of Boeotia to roast the seed-corn, so that the next year's crop would fail to sprout. Everything happened as she planned. The harvest failed and Athamas sent messengers to Delphi to consult the oracle. But Ino had bribed a messenger and he returned with this false reply: 'The god demands the sacrifice of Phrixus.'

With tears in his eyes, Athamas led his son to a mountain top and raised the sacrificial blade. Suddenly, a golden ram appeared — sent, it is said, by Hera, or perhaps by Zeus, who disliked human sacrifice — and whisked both Phrixus and Helle onto its back. In a moment, the ram was galloping away, making short work of distance and landscape, heading for the unknown east. The children clutched onto the fleece, but when the ram came to the narrow sea that separates Europe and Asia, Helle lost her hold and was drowned in the water afterwards named the Hellespont in her honour. Passing the southern shore of the Black Sea, the ram ran on with Phrixus to the land of Colchis, where King Aeëtes ruled. This king received Phrixus kindly, and in thanksgiving for a safe deliverance, they sacrificed the ram to Zeus. The bright skin was hung in an oak-grove

dedicated to Ares and guarded by a dragon. This was the Golden Fleece.

Jason, whose story now begins, was born in Thessaly. His grandfather was the king of Iolcus, brother to King Athamas of Boeotia. When Jason's grandfather died, his step-son, Pelias, usurped the throne from Jason's father, Aeson, the rightful heir. Then, when an oracle warned Pelias that he would be killed by a one-sandalled man belonging to the family of Aeson, Pelias put to death as many of that family as he could find. Aeson's little son, Jason, was sent secretly to live with Cheiron on Mount Pelion.

After many years with Cheiron, Jason was ready for the world and set out first for Iolcus where a festival to Poseidon was about to be celebrated. It is difficult to please the gods. In honouring Poseidon, Pelias neglected Hera, and she was angry with him. Disguised as an old woman, she met Jason by a swollen stream and asked his help to cross the water. He took her on his back, but in mid-stream she grew so heavy that Jason staggered and lost a sandal on the river's stony bed. With Hera's thanks he went on his way, a carefree youth who took no account of a lost sandal.

At the festival in Iolcus, Pelias was aghast when he noticed this tall, one-sandalled stranger in the crowd, and even more afraid when he learned who it was. With many fair words he pretended to recognize Jason's claim to the kingdom. But first he begged the young man to bring a certain Golden Fleece back from the far land of Colchis, claiming that all the lands of Phrixus' kinsmen — including Iolcus — were under a curse so long as that fleece hung in the distant grove and Phrixus' ghost still wandered far from home, dead but unburied in distant Colchis.

Jason, to whom adventure was the salt of life, agreed immediately. Heralds went to the ends of Hellas to summon princes and heroes to the expedition. The boat-builder Argus constructed a large, fine ship, the first with fifty oars ever to be made. He named it the *Argo* and Athene fastened to the bow a beam of oak, taken from Zeus' sacred grove at Dodona and capable of oracular speech. Tiphys, best of navigators, was the helmsman and Lynceus, whose eyesight was as keen as an eagle's, was the look-out. Many great heroes, all in search of danger and adventure, joined the crew, among them Orpheus, the poet, and Heracles, whom many wished to make their leader. But Heracles refused; for it was Jason's expedition, and Heracles had too many pressing works to stay with the ship till the journey's end.

Leaving the harbour at Pagasae in Thessaly, with powerful oarsmen straining at each oar, the *Argo* headed for the open Aegean. The sun shimmered bravely on armour and polished shields as the pilot set course for Lemnos, on the way to the Black Sea. Landing on Lemnos, the Argonauts were surprised to meet only bands of women. Some time before, the wives of the island had so neglected the rites of Aphrodite that the goddess punished them with an unmistakeable stench. In disgust, the men of Lemnos raided the Thracian mainland for more sweet-smelling mates, abandoning the island and their women. When the Argonauts arrived, the women planned to fight them off until an ancient nurse prudently reminded them that without men their race would die out. 'The best plan,' she advised, 'would be to welcome these bold mariners and join with them in love, so that we may bring forth a new breed of islanders.'

As this seemed good sense, with becoming modesty Hypsipyle laid claim to Jason and offered him the vacant kingship, which he declined. The Argonauts, however, surrounded by so many frank and engaging women, were reluctant to leave. They spent many happy days in Lemnos, as a result of which not a few children were later born, including two which Jason fathered by Hypsipyle. And who knows how long they might have remained in this blissful state had not Heracles, ever the man of action, been impatient to go on? He strode through the town, beating on doors with his club, driving his companions to the beach, back to the open, adventurous seas.

Sailing north to Samothrace, the Argonauts were initiated into the mysteries of Persephone, as was the custom with sailors who wished for a safe return. The *Argo* slipped quietly through the Hellespont at night, to avoid the unfriendly Trojans, and landed on the peninsula of the Doliones, where they were well received and feasted. In return for this kindness, Heracles shot certain unruly earth-born giants who were causing trouble, and the Argonauts departed with good feeling on both sides. But the ship could make little progress against boisterous winds, and, as dusk was falling, the pilot went about and headed for an anchorage. When they landed the Argonauts were surprised to find themselves under attack by well-armed men. In the dark they beat off the attack, and in the morning discovered, to their dismay, that they had killed a war-party of Doliones, including the king, who had mistaken the returning *Argo* for a pirate ship. Though Jason and his friends gave the king a noble funeral, and instituted funeral games, still the ship remained penned in by the weather. Day followed day with no hope of continuing their voyage until Mopsus, who understood the language of birds, learned from the storm-bird which lives among the seaweed that the goddess Rhea was angry at the death of her earth-born giants. They appeased the goddess with offerings, the favourable wind returned and the ship moved on.

Now the ship made good time, scudding along the coast of Mysia, until Heracles, who always pulled his oar with exceptional force, snapped the blade. Grateful for the rest, the crew shipped oars and drifted to the land. While fires were being lit and preparations made for supper, Heracles went off in search of timber and young Hylas, his favourite and his squire, took a pitcher to fetch fresh water. Hylas soon found a pool, but, as he dipped his pitcher in the water, the water nymphs

were so taken with his beauty that they pulled him under the surface. When the youth did not return, Heracles and Arcadian Polyphemus began to search for him. Calling his name, they went further and further into the rough country until they lost all touch with the ship. Jason was impatient to depart and at last, deciding to leave them behind, he gave the order to cast off.

Coming next to the country of Bebrycos in Bithynia, the Argonauts were challenged by King Amycus, a son of Poseidon, to choose one of their number for a boxing match. Luckily, Polydeuces, one of the adventurers, was the most skilful boxer of his age. He willingly drew on the rawhide gloves while Amycus wrapped his fists in cruel, metal-studded thongs. Then they set to, the muscular king making bull-like rushes and swinging with wild power, while Polydeuces dodged and countered with precise jabs and hooks. Back and forth they swayed in the ring of spectators, until Polydeuces caught his tiring opponent off-guard and crushed his skull with a mighty blow. The watching citizens broke into the ring, brandishing clubs, but the Argonauts were expecting some trickery from these barbarians and easily drove them back to the palace, which they then sacked and burned. After sacrificing twenty bulls to Poseidon, to ward off his wrath at the death of Amycus, the Argonauts hurried away.

The *Argo* was now heading for the dangerous, narrow strait of the Bosphorus, and Jason pulled over to the Thracian shore, to ask blind King Phineus of Salmydessus for advice. Some say Phineus had been blinded for guiding Phrixus on his way, others that his prophetic powers offended the gods, who made him choose between death and blindness. When he chose blindness, Helius took it as a personal insult against his divine gift of sunlight and further punished the king with two Harpies, bestial, bird-women who fouled his food at every meal. Phineus agreed to give advice if the Argonauts would rid him of these Harpies. When the next meal was ready, and the filthy beasts came hopping out of the sky, two of the Argonauts, Calais and Zetes, winged sons of the North Wind,

rose with their swords into the air and chased the screaming creatures away for ever. Then Phineus gladly told them how to find the best way through the Bosphorus, and in particular how to navigate the Clashing Rocks of the Symplegades. Beyond these the stormy waters of the Black Sea spread out to where Colchis lay, under the shadow of the Caucasian mountains.

Under a pall of sea-mist, the Symplegades marked the entrance to the Bosphorus, clashing back and forth and crushing in their jaws any vessel daring enough to try the narrow passage. Following the advice of Phineus, the *Argo's* helmsman released a dove to fly through the gap and steered the ship close behind. As the rocks nipped tail feathers from the dove and then sprang back, the rowers heaved on their oars and, driven on by urgent music from Orpheus' lyre, hurtled the *Argo* through the narrows. The rocky jaws caught only the extreme end of the stern-post. Having missed their prey, the Symplegades retreated and stood still, for the gods allowed them no more mischief.

Out at last on the broad highway of the Black Sea, the ship followed the southern coast, landing each evening for food and rest. Now a number of misfortunes hit the crew. Hunting for fresh meat by the River Lycus, Idmon was gashed by the tusks of a boar and bled to death. Soon after, Tiphys, the pilot, grew sick and also died. With a new helmsman the *Argo* passed the land of the Amazon women, went on to that of the Chalybes, who knew nothing but iron-working and neither farmed nor hunted, and then passed the Mossynoechi, a warlike people who gave great offence by their bad morals. These were barbarians, living far from the lands favoured by the gods of Olympus, and their manners and customs were strange.

Dangers of another kind awaited the ship by the isles of Ares. The Stymphalian birds, driven to these barren rocks by Heracles' sixth labour, attacked the *Argo* with their dart-like feathers. The crew were forced to shelter beneath their shields, raising ferocious war-cries and clashing weapons to frighten the birds away. At these same rocks, the

Argonauts rescued four shipwrecked sailors who proved to be the sons of Phrixus, wrecked in the course of a journey back to their father's homeland. Though Jason welcomed them, to make up the depleted numbers on the rowing benches, these sons were not anxious to desecrate the holy spot where their father had hung the Golden Fleece. But the Argonauts had saved their lives, so the four sons of Phrixus made an offering to Ares and took their places at the oars among the other heroes. Without further incident, the *Argo* reached its destination, the mouth of the River Phasis in the land of Colchis. On one bank of the river stood the city of Aea and the palace of King Aeëtes; and on the other bank hung the Golden Fleece.

Jason threw out the anchor-stone well away from the city and called together his companions to decide what they should do. Some were for taking the Fleece by force, but Jason suggested that they try argument and diplomacy first. With the four sons of Phrixus he walked the river bank to the shining city of Aea, past the stables at the eastern end of the world where Helius stalled the horses of the sun-chariot. Aeëtes met Jason with suspicion, and though the Argonaut offered to wipe out all the enemies of the king, Aeëtes was not impressed. He did not like the peoples from south of the Bosphorus, and with black looks he advised the Argonauts to leave before they had their tongues torn out, or worse. He would not give up the Golden Fleece. Such threats could not deter the heroes and, as Jason kept his temper and continued to press his forceful arguments, Aeëtes thought that the best way to remove these interfering strangers was to agree to their request, but to impose outrageous conditions upon them. He would only surrender the Fleece, he said, if Jason could yoke two fire-breathing, brazen-footed bulls of Hephaestus, plough the Field of Ares, and sow it with some of the dragon's teeth which Cadmus had used at Thebes.

This was a hard, if not impossible task and Jason went away sick at heart. But the great goddesses Hera and Athene were devoted to Jason's cause and were already considering how to help him.

They decided to use the king's daughter, Medea. Medea was not only beautiful, but also a priestess of Hecate and a sorceress. So the Olympian goddesses approached Aphrodite and she sent mischievous Eros to loose one of his arrows at Medea, to instil in her heart a passion for Jason. Secretly, in the night, Medea declared her love to Jason and promised to see him safely through his trials if he would take her with him as his wife.

When this was agreed, Medea gave Jason a magic ointment to spread on his body and his armour, assuring him that this would protect him from the fiery breath of the bulls. Then, by his own strength, Jason yoked the bulls and ploughed the field before nightfall. He sowed the dragon's teeth, and when armed men sprang up he foiled them as Medea had advised him. Like Cadmus before him, he tossed a boulder among the ranks of the warriors, who then began to fight among themselves, to their own destruction. With the task complete, Jason went in triumph to Aeëtes and claimed the Fleece. But the king would not keep his promise. Instead of rewarding Jason, Aeëtes began preparations to destroy the *Argo* and her crew.

There was no time to lose. Before Aeëtes could act, Medea led the Argonauts to the grove where the ever-watchful dragon guarded the Fleece, throwing its great coils around the tree and hissing a warning. Medea had brought an infusion made from juniper, and this she flung into the dragon's eyes, causing the beast to fall into a deep sleep. Jason ripped the Golden Fleece from the tree and the Argonauts ran for the beach, with Medea and her little half-brother Apsyrtus in their midst. By now, the alarm was raised. The soldiers of Aeëtes were close behind, and in the running skirmish several of the heroes were wounded, but all reached the *Argo*. Tumbling aboard, the Argonauts dug their oars so deep that the water seemed to boil. But already the king's warships were out of the harbour and on course to cut off the *Argo's* retreat. Medea, seeing that the Argonauts were outnumbered and heading for trouble, performed a pitiless act: she killed Apsyrtus, dismembered his body, and threw his limbs, one by one, into the

## The Black Sea

This was called *Pontos* by the Ionian Greeks, who were the first to build themselves cities on its coasts. To sailors *Pontos* meant 'the open sea' and it was open in the sense that, unlike the Aegean, there are almost no islands in it. It was often referred to as the *Pontos Axeinos*, — the 'unfriendly sea', because its coasts were inhabited by hostile natives. After a time this was changed to *Euxeinos*, 'friendly', either because the Greeks now knew the natives better or in the hope that changing the name would help to improve its nature. Neither the Minoans nor the Mycenaeans visited it, probably because the passage of the Dardanelles and the Bosphoros is very difficult for a sailing vessel unless the winds and the currents have been carefully studied. The Ionian Greeks discovered how to make the passage and began trading there in the fifth century B C. Soon their trading posts became colonies and the colonies became cities, trading in wines, olive oil and works of Greek craftsmen, all of which they exchanged with the fierce Scythian chiefs for wheat for shipment to Greece.

The quest for the Golden Fleece in Colchis (now the Black Sea coast of Soviet Georgia) is thought by some to reflect the real-life trade in gold with the natives of that area. The gold it is said, was found in the local streams and extracted by hanging a woolly fleece in the stream. Other scholars are suspicious of any such attempt to give a rational explanation for mythical fantasies.

path of the enemy, so that the Colchians, out of piety, had to stop to recover the remains of the little prince. By this cruel sacrifice, the pursuers were shaken off and the *Argo* sped away to the north-west.

# The voyage home

Now the ship was in uncertain waters, driven into new seas and across parts of the world unknown to southern navigators. Under the guidance of Hera, the helmsman turned the rudder, but he did not know where he was going. Some say that the Argonauts paused for rest at the mouth of the Danube, where the Colchians caught up with them. After a fight, the *Argo* fled inland, going by rivers and overland portage to the storm-lashed northern sea, then returning along a dangerous coast to the Pillars of Heracles. Others say that the Danube took the adventurers to the mysterious River Eridanos, which led after many hazardous passages back to the Adriatic. Perhaps the truth was in the knowledge of the gods only, who led the ship to the edge of the world and then brought it back along the stream of Oceanus. However they went, at last the Argonauts recognized familiar waters and stopped at the island of Elba to give thanks and to wipe from their brows the sweat of their long effort. They rubbed the cool pebbles over their tired bodies, and ever after this the pebbles on the beach have had the look of human skin.

Now, just as the way home seemed clear, another obstacle blocked their path. At Corfu, the oracular beam in the prow of the ship, taken from Zeus' sacred oak at Dodona, sternly reminded them that they were still stained with the blood of Apsyrtus. The ship would make no further progress until the crew was purified. Wearily, the Argonauts set out once more, searching for the island of Aeaea, where they hoped that Circe, Medea's aunt and a great sorceress, would use her powers on their behalf. When they found her, Circe was reluctant to help to cleanse so grave a crime, but she was persuaded by Medea's begging pleas and, at last, purified from blood-guilt, the Argonauts were free to return.

With gentle winds and following seas, the *Argo* went swiftly away, for Hera had asked the sea goddess Thetis to smooth the path of the ship. Setting a new course, the Argonauts came within reach of the green, beguiling island where the Sirens, half-bird and half-maiden, tempted travellers to their death with songs that ravished the ear. As the hearts of the Argonauts were drawn towards this deadly music, Orpheus rose from the rowing bench and with his divine lyre drowned out the Siren sounds with more seductive music of his own. Only Butes succumbed to the lure of the Sirens, abandoning himself to the sea and the Sirens' song while the ship went on without him.

After many days of quiet sailing, the *Argo* came to the tempestuous gorge where the rock of Scylla lay on one side and the whirlpool of Charybdis on the other. The air was full of the noise of roaring water and the pilot held his breath in terror as the spray broke over the mast. But Thetis and her Nereid sea nymphs had not deserted them. Thetis herself laid her steady hand on the helm and the Nereids guarded the ship from the dangers of the sea and rocks. Passing thankfully into calm waters, the Argonauts sailed on to a peaceful haven on the island of the Phaeacians.

The peace was soon shattered. A Colchian fleet, which had been hunting the Argonauts far and wide, now caught up with them, and with a menacing display of force demanded the return of both Medea and the Fleece. Medea, who had good reason to fear the anger of her father, begged the king and queen of the Phaeacians to save her, and the royal couple, anxious to avoid bloodshed on their island, devised a plan to help her. Having warned Medea and Jason to marry secretly in the night, King Alcinous told the Colchians that he would arbitrate on the matter and give a decision in the morning. Next day, he delivered his judgement: 'If Medea is still a virgin, she must go back to Colchis; if not, she may remain with Jason.' Jason claimed Medea as his lawful bride, and the Colchian fleet went away angry but outwitted.

## The story and the voyage

The story that a prince called Jason made a voyage in a ship called *Argo* is mentioned by Homer and also by Hesiod. The version of the story given here comes from a long poem written in Alexandria or Rhodes by a poet called Apollonius a century and a half after the conquests of Alexander the Great. By that time the story had received many additions and the goal of the voyage had been transferred from the Mediterranean to the Black (Euxine) Sea. The return journey of the Argonauts by the Ister (Danube) and Eridanos (the River Po, in North Italy), the western Mediterranean, Corfu, Libya and Crete gave Apollonius the opportunity to include a multitude of adventures with characters from other stories, such as the Sirens, the Phaeacians, and Circe. It also shows that Greek knowledge of the geography of Europe, though still hazy about the inland areas, was much more extensive than at the time of Homer.

Apollonius was born in Alexandria in Egypt, but spent part of his life on the island of Rhodes and so is usually referred to as 'Apollonius Rhodius'. In the five centuries which separate him from Homer, the nature of Greek poetry had greatly changed. Greek poets in the third and second centuries BC were generally learned men and they wrote for a highly cultured readership. In consequence their poems abound in references to antiquarian lore and obscure mythology. Apollonius was no exception. During part of his lifetime he was librarian at the extensive library of Greek books which the Ptolemies, the Macedonian Greek rulers of Egypt, had founded and maintained at Alexandria.

Most modern readers find much of the original *Argonautica* tedious but there are some fine passages—in particular the description of Medea's state of mind when she falls in love with the handsome stranger Jason and has to choose between loyalty to her father and her passion for Jason.

Once more the Argonauts rowed on but now, Boreas, the North Wind, blew up a sudden storm which drove their ship helplessly towards Africa and left it high and dry on the desert shore at Syrtes. With the help of the three goatskin-clad goddesses, who watched over the deserts of Libya, and of Poseidon, they managed to roll the ship first to the calm waters of Lake Tritonis, and then back to the more familiar seas. From Libya, the Argonauts headed north, much relieved to be back with the winds and the waters that they knew. When they approached Crete and wanted to land for supplies, the bronze giant Talos, guardian of the island, drove them off with huge rocks. Medea, however, offered to tame the giant with her magic charms. She called out to him with flattery and sweet words, tempting him to try an immortal potion. The drink she gave him sent him fast asleep instead. The *Argo* stole into the bay and Medea pulled out of the giant the single bronze pin which stopped up his veins. Talos slept on, while his life-blood drained away, and the *Argo* passed by him safely. And at long last, after an age of trial and danger, the ship moved serenely through the well-remembered islands of the Cyclades, up the length of Euboea, and into the sheltered bay of Pagasae. The heroes were home.

No-one was there to meet them. The beach was empty and no flags waved from Iolcus, where friends and relatives had long ago given up hope of a safe return. Pelias still ruled the kingdom and still persecuted the family of Jason. The Argonauts dispersed to their distant homes, leaving Jason and Medea to face the cruel rancour of the king.

Jason could see no way to attack Pelias in his own city, but crafty Medea still had her magic powers. Knowing how old and feeble Pelias was, she came to him disguised as an ancient nurse and offered him an elixir of youth. Pelias was suspicious and wished to see how it worked, so Medea made a bath of her most potent magic herbs into which she put pieces of a tough old ram. When the mixture was boiled, a young lamb came gambolling out of the cauldron. Pelias and his daughters were convinced. Medea hypnotized the

king, and his loving daughters cut him limb from limb while Medea prepared a new magic mixture. But this time she put in different herbs; no youthful prince stepped from the cauldron's brew and Pelias was dead beyond recall.

Although Pelias was justly punished for his many abominable crimes, his son Acastus was tied by family duty to avenge him and he ordered Jason and Medea to leave Iolcus for ever. They went without regret, for Jason hoped to win a richer kingdom. First, however, he travelled to Orchomenus, the foremost settlement of the Minyan people, and hung the Golden Fleece there in the temple of Zeus. Then he sailed the *Argo* to the Isthmus of Corinth, hauled the ship from the water and dedicated it to Poseidon.

Medea had a family claim to the throne of Corinth and when the old king died, the citizens accepted Jason and Medea as their new rulers. For ten years they reigned happily and the land prospered. Then Jason wished to set his wife aside, some say because he feared her wild and dangerous temperament, but more certainly because he had fallen in love with Glauce, daughter of a nearby king. He should have known better than to expect Medea to give way gracefully. With her usual cunning she pretended submission, and she even sent Glauce a robe and a garland for her wedding day. But the gifts were poisoned. Glauce and her father, who tried to save her, perished in burning agony. Then, in a final act of barbarian savagery, Medea murdered her own two children by Jason and fled in a winged chariot to Athens.

As to Jason himself, his last days were short, sad and embittered. Some say he was so much under the spell of the sorceress Medea, to whom he owed both his success and misery, that he helped to murder his own children. Certainly, he did not live long after Medea fled. It was rumoured that he killed himself as a penance for his children's death. But those with better knowledge report that, when he was sitting under the familiar timbers of the *Argo* to ponder his wretched fate, a baulk of wood fell from the dried-out hull and killed him.

# THE TALE OF TROY

## The city of Troy

Zeus, king of gods and men, came suddenly, in the form of a swan, to Leda, wife of Tyndareus of Sparta. In a moment of fear and exaltation, the great bird took her, and Leda brought forth an egg from which hatched Helen, the most beautiful of all women. For mankind, what consequences flow from the games of the gods! In that egg were the seeds of a ten-year war, the furious clash of heroes, the death of many on the burnt Asian plain, and, at last, the fall and ruin of the city of Troy.

First, learn the foundation of this famous city, whose tale the poets tell and whose fate has filled our hearts with wonder and pity from generation to generation.

Dardanus, a son of Zeus and a native of Samothrace, fled from his island home because of the crimes of his family. In shame, he went to exile in Phrygia, on the east of the Aegean. There, finding favour with the king, he settled in the country at the mouth of the Hellespont. He prospered, and his heirs built on his good beginning. In the course of time, his descendant, Ilus, won a wrestling match for which the prize was fifty youths and fifty maidens. He was also given a spotted cow and told to take his band of young people to wherever the cow should lead him and to found a city on that spot. The cow lay down by a low hill on the plain near the entrance to the Hellespont, and there Ilus marked out the boundaries of a city which was sometimes called Ilium, after its founder, but more usually called Troy.

When the bounds were marked and Ilus had prayed to the gods for a sign of good luck, he discovered next morning a large wooden statue lying in front of his tent. This was the Palladium, the image that the goddess Athene had made in memory of her childhood friend Pallas. Apollo, who knew what a powerful token the Palladium was, now appeared and advised Ilus always to guard and respect it; for as long as Troy preserved the statue, the city itself would come to no harm. Ilus placed the Palladium in a shrine on the citadel and appointed priests to look after it.

The city grew with mixed fortunes. Overlooking the trade routes to the Black Sea, and at the crossroads of Europe and Asia, Troy soon became rich and powerful. But this success attracted the enmity of the less fortunate, and in their pride the rulers of Troy sometimes forgot courtesy towards others and humility towards the gods. King Laomedon tried to cheat great Heracles and died for his foolishness. His son Priam took this as a warning and ruled with greater foresight, restoring the prosperity of the city. There was an ancient tradition which, despite the presence of the Palladium, prophesied ill-luck for Troy, so Priam took careful account of the signs from the gods. And when his wife Hecabe dreamed that she gave birth to a flaming torch which burned down the city, Priam took this to mean that his expected child would be the cause of disaster. When the baby was born, King Priam ordered the boy to be left to die on Mount Ida.

The Fates decreed that the baby should not die. Suckled at first by a she-bear, the child was then found by a herdsman who named him Paris and raised him with his own family. Paris soon outstripped the other boys in courage and beauty. At an early age he drove off some cattle thieves and won the name Alexander, or 'Defender of Men'. He was the best of all the herdsmen, so when Priam sent an envoy to choose a bull for sacrifice, it was Paris who drove the bull to Troy. Now, this

sacrifice was part of the funeral games which the king held each year, in honour of the little son he had abandoned and who was presumed to be dead. Arriving at Troy as an unknown, handsome countryman, Paris entered the games and did so well in the foot-races and the boxing that the princes were jealous and decided to kill him. Just as one, Deiphobus, was about to cut him down, Cassandra, Priam's prophetic daughter, called out: 'Do not raise your hand against your brother!' Astonished, the princes stood back. But when they and their father Priam reflected on how brave and handsome this young man was, they gladly gave Paris his rightful place in the royal household.

# The judgement of Paris

As Paris was growing up on the slopes of Mount Ida, Zeus finally resolved an age-old problem. Long ago, almost before time had a meaning, Zeus had been warned that any child born to the sea goddess Thetis was destined to be mightier than its father. Zeus himself desired Thetis, but he restrained his passion and looked for a human husband for the goddess, by whom she would have only mortal children. At last, his choice fell on Peleus, son of Aeacus, who was at that time under the protection of the Centaur Cheiron, on Mount Pelion in Thessaly.

Now, wise Cheiron realized that no immortal would be flattered by marriage to a mere human, and that Thetis, who, like her father Nereus, could change her shape at will, would be hard to catch. On Cheiron's instructions, Peleus waited for the Nereid as she rose from the sea for her midday rest. While Thetis dozed in a secluded cave, Peleus crept silently up to her, took hold of her, and somehow kept a desperate grip as she went through puzzling transformations, from fire to water, from lion to serpent, and even to a giant ink-squirting cuttlefish.

He would not let go, and at last Thetis surrendered to him and lay peacefully in his arms, for this, after all, was the will of mighty Zeus, father of gods and men.

This resolution was pleasing to the gods, and all the Olympians came to Mount Pelion to celebrate the wedding feast. It was a joyful occasion, enlivened by the wine which Dionysus brought, and many glorious gifts were presented to the bride and groom. But the goddess Eris, Strife, had not been invited and she was determined to spoil the day. While the three great goddesses Hera, Athene and Aphrodite stood arm in arm together, in a rare display of harmony, Eris threw at their feet a golden apple on which was written: 'To the fairest.' At once, stirred up by ancient rivalries, each goddess claimed the apple. The argument grew loud and rancorous and might have led to blows had not Zeus intervened. Offering to put the dispute to impartial judgement, he summoned his messenger Hermes: 'Take this matter to Mount Ida, in Mysia, where you will find a young man tending cattle who is as wise as he is handsome. His name is Paris. Let him be the judge.'

Away the Olympians went to Mount Ida, but Paris was abashed by the presence of the goddesses. Their glory overwhelmed him. He was, he protested, only a herdsman and unequal to the task they set him. Hermes assured him that when Zeus willed it, anything was possible, and the goddesses, one by one, took him aside and pressed their claims.

Hera, the Queen of Heaven, offered him great wealth and earthly power. Unconquerable Athene promised him wisdom and success in battle. But Aphrodite, goddess of love, took him by the hand and whispered of the secret movements of the heart. She said he was so handsome. Why, his good looks would make him pleasing even to Helen of Sparta, who alone among women was as beautiful as Aphrodite herself. He had heard that Helen was married? Was that the difficulty?

'Pouf,' Aphrodite continued, 'such things are nothing in affairs of the heart. I could be persuaded to influence her on your behalf. I think I can guarantee that she will fall in love with you.'

Paris took the golden apple and gave it to Aphrodite.

# Helen of Sparta

Helen came to womanhood in the court of Leda and Tyndareus. Growing more beautiful by the day, she made the palace at Sparta a magnet for the princes of the surrounding lands, all eager for her hand in marriage. Agamemnon, lord of Argos and the most powerful of kings, was not a suitor because he was already married to Helen's half-sister Clytaemnestra. But Menelaus, his brother from Achaea, was an ardent wooer, as were such other heroes as Ajax, Diomedes, Philoctetes and Menestheus. Odysseus also came to Sparta, though he knew that his poor, distant patrimony in Ithaca gave him little chance in these glamorous stakes. But Odysseus was always willing to watch and learn.

Tyndareus did not want to offend any of these great men. Uncertain what to do, he turned to Odysseus who advised him to make all the suitors swear an oath, to promise that, whoever was the lucky man, all the others would defend him to the death against those who might attempt to ruin his good fortune. The oath was solemnly sworn and Tyndareus gave Helen to Menelaus, the richest of the princes. He marked the occasion with an offering to the gods, but it was the ill fortune of mankind that he forgot to include Aphrodite.

Tyndareus died and so too did his famous sons Castor and Polydeuces. Menelaus became king of Sparta, where he lived peacefully with his wife Helen, who gave birth to three children. Then, on a north-east wind, the Fates brought the ships of Paris to the home of Helen. The Trojans came under the excuse of an embassy, or, some say, because Paris wanted Menelaus to purify him after an accidental killing. But in truth, Paris had only one object: to return in triumph with the woman Aphrodite had promised him. Cassandra cried out as her brother sailed from Troy, for her prophetic dreams had shown her terror and death. And Oenone, the water nymph who loved Paris, warned him with tears not to go. But, urged on by Aphrodite, he heard nothing but the sighs of love

## Who fought at Troy?

Homer's *Iliad* describes the events of no more than fifty days in the ninth year of the ten-year siege of Troy. Other poets, later than Homer, filled the gaps he left with epics describing the events leading up to the expedition, the battle fought between Achilles and the Amazon queen, the killing of Achilles by Paris and Apollo, and the capture and sack of Troy. These epics have all been lost and we only know of them because later poets and dramatists refer to them. References were also made to them by ancient scholars writing in one of the new cultural centres established after Alexander the Great's conquest of the Persian empire, particularly the centre at Alexandria in Egypt.

The Trojan war is remembered as a battle between the combined army of Greece (Hellas) and the people of the city of Troy. In Homer the only warriors called Hellenes are a small group of warriors coming from a small area in north central Greece. Agamemnon's army as a whole is called usually 'the Achaeans', sometimes 'the Argives' and sometimes 'the Danaans'.

In the second book of the *Iliad* there is a long list of the contingents of troops who went to Troy in support of Agamemnon, giving the names of their commanders and the numbers of ships they commanded. This list is often suspected of being a later addition, but it does mirror surprisingly accurately the geography of Mycenaean Greece in so far as this has been established by archaeological excavations. It contains many cities that had been prosperous in the late Bronze Age but must have been insignificant ruins by the time of Homer.

The list of Mycenaean cities and their rulers is, unfortunately, not proof that these were the actual warriors who fought at Troy, although the Greeks of Homer's time accepted it as historical. Today, scholars account for the many oddities in the list by supposing that the Athenians tampered with the text to their own advantage when it was being edited for copying in the sixth century B C.

and hurried to the rewards of the heart.

Menelaus welcomed Paris in a manner worthy of a great prince, with feasting and entertainment. That evening, as they all sat at the banquet, Helen and Paris exchanged long looks. Tutored by Aphrodite, Helen understood the message of his eyes and she blushed. On the second day, Menelaus, a stolid, unobservant fellow, left for a visit to Crete. That same night, Helen and Paris eloped. On a little island, near the harbour, Paris set up a shrine to Aphrodite; then the lovers set sail for Troy with a large part of the Spartan palace treasure and with five royal serving-women. Angry Hera buffeted them with storms, and the ship had to beat about in some danger between Cyprus and Sidon. But they reached Troy safely, and the Trojans, whatever misgivings they might have had concerning Paris' rash act, were captivated by the extraordinary beauty of Helen. Even King Priam, who knew only too well the warnings of doom, lost his heart to her and swore an oath never to let her go. The fate of Troy was sealed.

## Preparations for war

Formerly, men of sense did not make a great stir when a prince or hero ran away with another man's wife. It was clear, in most cases, that the women were not taken by force but, on the contrary, consented to their abduction, and who would make a fuss over women acting from their own free will? But when the gods intervene and manipulate the minds of men, the smallest breeze swells suddenly to an overwhelming storm which bears all before it. For the sake of a single Spartan girl, kings collected vast armies and took the road to death on the plains of Troy.

When Helen was gone, Hera sent the messenger Iris flying to Crete, to bring Menelaus home. He went straight to the court of Agamemnon at Mycenae, and pressed his brother to remind all Helen's former suitors of the oath they had sworn. Unwilling to raise up the devils of war, Agamemnon sent envoys to Troy, but when they returned empty-handed he agreed to place himself at the head of an invading army. Nestor, the wise old greybeard, was summoned from Pylus, and with his diplomatic help Menelaus made the rounds of the courts, letting the suitors know, in his bluff way, what their oath demanded from them. Many were not inclined to leave home, but Hera pricked their consciences and they began to prepare their forces.

Agamemnon, great overlord of all Argos, was recognized as leader of the expedition, with wronged Menelaus at his side and old Nestor as chief counsellor. Others gathered from far and wide. From Salamis came the greater Ajax, head and shoulders taller than other men and, as a warrior, second only to Achilles. Though somewhat slow-witted, Ajax was the most courageous fighter, always in the forefront of battle. Heracles had wrapped him at birth in his lion-skin, making his body safe from wounds, except around the armpit and neck where the lion-skin had not quite met. Ajax's one fault was a boastful pride which made him resent the achievements of others and even scorn the help of the gods. Later, this pride led to his death in shame and madness.

His namesake, the lesser Ajax, commanded the men from Locris. He was a good fighter, swift and nimble, and he threw a deadly spear. But he was a violent, rude, untrustworthy fellow, usually accompanied by a tame serpent which followed him like a dog. He, too, was given to boasting, and he also paid for this with his life when, shipwrecked near Naxos on the return from Troy, he bragged that he had escaped despite the gods. Immediately, Poseidon threw him into the sea and drowned him. Foremost among the other warriors was Diomedes, son of Tydeus, a soldier who won his fame in the campaign of the Epigoni against Thebes. He was a favourite of Athene, doubly valuable as a daring fighter but also as a strategist and a master of the unexpected. When he and Odysseus put their heads together, they promised much mischief for the Trojans.

Many other contingents converged on the

assembly place at Aulis. Some suitors tried to evade their oath, like Cinyras of Cyprus, who promised fifty ships but sent only one real one and forty-nine clay models. Apollo struck him dead. The Cretan Idomeneus offered a grand fleet of a hundred ships if he were given pride of place in the invasion. But Philoctetes was just as important to the allies, though he brought only the bow of Heracles. Two men, however, outweighed all others in the minds of the commanders. Without Odysseus and Achilles, the army would be deprived of its brain and its strongest arm, so Agamemnon and Menelaus made great efforts to find and persuade them to join the expedition.

In search of Odysseus, Menelaus and Palamedes set out for Ithaca. Odysseus was at home, but he did not want to join. He had not long been married to Penelope, with whom he lived very happily, and an oracle had warned him that he risked twenty years of separation if he left for Troy. When the envoys arrived, Odysseus feigned madness. Putting on a rustic felt cap, he yoked an ox and an ass and began to plough, sowing salt into the furrow instead of seed. But Palamedes was not deceived. He took baby Telemachus from Penelope's arms and placed him in the path of the plough. Odysseus was not mad enough to drive over his son, so he reined in his strange team and admitted his deceit. He went reluctantly to Troy, where he saved many a bad day by his intelligence and cunning. But he never forgave Palamedes.

Though the presence of Odysseus was a triumph for Agamemnon, even more vital for the success of the expedition was Achilles, son of Peleus and the sea goddess Thetis. A prophecy warned that Troy would never be taken without this most powerful, bravest and most handsome of all warriors.

Thetis, by the will of Zeus, had married the mortal Peleus, but she did not give up the hope of having immortal children. As each of her babies was born, she held the child over fire, as Demeter had done with Demophoön, to burn away mortality. But the gods would not grant the precious gift of immortality and each child perished in the flames. When Achilles, the seventh child,

arrived, Peleus snatched him from the fire and substituted the thigh-bone of a giant. Baulked of her desire, Thetis gave Achilles the next best thing to immortality. To make him invulnerable, she dipped him in the waters of the Styx, holding the babe by the heel, which alone remained a point of weakness. Having done what she could for Achilles, and disgusted with the company of humans, Thetis deserted her family and returned to the sea.

Thus abandoned by his mother, Achilles was sent by Peleus to Mount Pelion, to be brought up by the Centaur Cheiron, who had educated many heroes and knew how to bring the best out of noble young manhood. Excelling in all the many arts of hunting and war, Achilles was nearly full-grown when Paris abducted Helen. And though he was too young to be a suitor, and had taken no oath, Thetis knew with divine wisdom that her son would face death if he went to Troy, and she warned Peleus to hide him away: Achilles was sent to Lycomedes of Scyros, disguised as a girl. For some time he lived among the women but remembered his male nature sufficiently to father there the red-headed boy Neoptolemus.

Odysseus tracked Achilles to Scyros. He went there with Diomedes and Nestor, but Lycomedes innocently denied all knowledge of Achilles and allowed the envoys to search the palace. Odysseus, who guessed what might be going on, made a heap of many different gifts and invited the women of the palace to choose what they wanted. But when the women were gathered, Odysseus caused a trumpeter to blare out the alarm-call for battle. Most of the women fled, but one who seemed to be female stripped to the waist and rushed for the arms and armour included among the pile of gifts. With his disguise unmasked, and the light of battle in his eyes, Achilles was easily persuaded to join the expedition. Accompanied by his inseparable friend Patroclus, he set out for Aulis, eager to take his place at the head of his followers, the Myrmidons.

After long preparation the whole fleet was gathered at Aulis, in the shelter of the Gulf of

Euboea. Agamemnon sacrificed to Zeus and Apollo for success in the war. As he did so, a snake the colour of blood slid from the altar to a tree where it attacked and killed a mother bird and eight nestlings. The snake swallowed them all and then turned to a stone, a portent which the seer Calchas interpreted to mean that Troy would be taken, but not until after the ninth year. On this note of foreboding the fleet left, and the first luck of the expedition increased the feeling of calamity.

Aiming for Troy, the fleet blundered by mistake onto the coast of Mysia and, after some wasteful and unnecessary fighting, had to re-group at Aulis. And once again the Fates held them back. Agamemnon offended Artemis while hunting and the goddess prevented their departure until Agamemnon led his daughter Iphigenia to the sacrificial altar. Only then did the adverse winds drop and the ships set out again, this time in the proper direction. Pausing first as Lesbos, they sailed on to the island of Tenedos, from where the distant walls of Troy showed dimly in the morning light.

Tenes, king of Tenedos, was Apollo's son. Now, Achilles had been warned never to kill a child of Apollo and kept a servant whose special duty it was to keep this in his mind; for if he harmed Apollo's child, the god would certainly destroy him. But when Achilles saw a figure hurling rocks at the ships, he plunged into the water before the servant could caution him and ran the rock-thrower through with his sword. By ill-luck the rock-thrower was Tenes himself. This was disaster enough, but it was not the only ill-omened incident on Tenedos. Philoctetes, who had inherited Heracles' unerring bow, was bitten by a snake. The wound festered and Philoctetes' pain was so heart-rending, that Agamemnon ordered him to be abandoned on a rocky little island off Lemnos, where the poor man subsisted for several years on

## Did Homer's Troy ever exist?

To the ancient Greeks, Troy and the events of the Trojan war were historical events. They had no doubt that Troy was a city in the north-west corner of Asia Minor (now Turkey), near the Dardanelles and that it had fallen in the year 1183 BC.

In the nineteenth century, several travellers visited and even surveyed the legendary site but scholars were mostly sceptical that evidence could ever be found to confirm Homer's story. Then, in 1870, Heinrich Schliemann, a wealthy German merchant and amateur archaeologist, began to excavate an overgrown mound called Hisarlik whose position had long been thought to fit Homer's description of Troy and the traditions recorded by ancient historians. When he uncovered the remains of an ancient city, he had no hesitation in announcing that he had found Troy itself.

Archaeologists who followed Schliemann, using progressively more scientific methods, recognized the remains of nine superimposed cities, the first dating from around 3000 BC and the last a Roman city which had survived until the foundation of Constantinople. The most impressive of the early cities was destroyed about 1300 BC by an earthquake. Its successor, not nearly as impressive, was destroyed (by enemies rather than natural catastrophe) at the right time to be Homer's Troy and indeed, Mycenaean artefacts were found in its ruins. Schliemann claimed that jewellery he discovered could have belonged to Helen of Troy herself but later excavators realized that this jewellery had been found in a city that had been destroyed long before the Mycenaean civilization arose.

It seems very possible that the shining exploits of Homer's heroes embody traditions about an expedition against the less impressive city on the excavated site; but the real story will remain unknown unless and until someone, somewhere, digs up written references to it.

Schliemann went on to excavate the citadel at Mycenae, where he found spectacular burial sites, graves containing gold and silver vessels, bronze weapons and golden masks covering the faces of the royal dead. He, at least, had no doubt that he had discovered the grave of King Agamemnon himself.

fish and sea-birds. The episode cast a gloom over the fleet, so it was in sombre mood, already disheartened by equivocal signs from the gods, that the army of Agamemnon dropped anchor in the Asian shallows, where the Trojan plain stretched out to the nearby city.

All the portents seemed to indicate a long, weary time of grief and trial.

## Gods and heroes at war

Zeus willed the war. It was rumoured among men that the Father of the Gods resented the burden which mankind imposed upon the broad earth and arranged the Trojan conflict to make a void in the ranks of men. From the moment when Protesilaus, the first invader, leaped to the beach and was instantly slain by Hector, death flowed back and forth between the sea and the walls.

The Trojans were prepared for battle and ready to sell their lives dearly. The Trojan champion was Hector, first among Priam's fifty sons, and with him fought many of his brothers, including the trouble-maker Paris. Antenor was the king's chief minister, a man so fair and upright that even the enemy recognized his virtues. Aeneas, son of Aphrodite and Anchises, also spoke for peace and justice. He fought as a patriot, but regretted the headlong passion of Paris which had caused the sorry state of his country. Troy was strong and well-defended. Poseidon and Apollo had built the walls, and King Priam had many allies in Ionia and Phrygia who resented the over-proud invaders from across the Aegean Sea. For nine years the armies of Agamemnon, having little luck at the gates of Troy, harried these allies and sacked their cities.

Then, in the tenth year of war, a fateful quarrel split the besieging army. Achilles and his men attacked the city of Lyrnessus, west of Troy, and carried off two young girls whose beauty rivalled that of Aphrodite herself. Agamemnon, as commander of the force, claimed one, Cryseis, for himself, leaving the other, Briseis, to Achilles.

Cryseis, however, was Apollo's priestess and when a plague struck the camp, a seer advised she must be returned with due honours to her temple. Agamemnon at once obeyed—but claimed Achilles' prize, Briseis, in her place. Achilles, filled with disgust and rage, withdrew his mighty presence from the fight, and vowed he would not stir until full restitution had been made.

Now the Trojans took heart but still they could not quite press home their advantage. Sick of bloodshed, Hector tried to end the siege with a duel between Paris and Menelaus, the wrong-doer and the victim. And for a moment, when Menelaus had Paris at his mercy, it seemed that the war might end. But Aphrodite hid her favourite in a cloud and pulled him to safety behind the walls.

For the war was the plaything of the gods and they rolled men's lives like dice on the floor. Thetis demanded justice for her son Achilles, and Zeus had suffering in store for the Trojans yet. Apollo strengthened the arms of the defenders, and on the attackers' side Diomedes was so enraged by meddling deities that he wounded both Ares and Aphrodite, spilling their divine blood. But among the warriors, there was great weariness on both sides. A truce was arranged during which Odysseus led a deputation that tried and failed to placate the resentment of Achilles.

Fighting began again. In a daring night raid, Odysseus and Diomedes killed Rhesus, who was bringing Thracian allies to Troy, and captured his white horses which, had they entered the city, were fated to save the Trojans. Spurred on by Apollo the sons of Priam retaliated fiercely, breaking through the wooden palisade which guarded the Achaean ships and setting fire to part of the fleet. The Trojans seemed on the verge of triumph when Patroclus, Achilles' great friend, appeared wearing the arms and armour of the hero and frightened the Trojans into retreat. Patroclus chased them to the walls of Troy where Apollo himself had to turn back the attack. The god winded and disarmed Patroclus, then Hector killed him with a single blow and stripped Achilles' armour from the body.

At last, grief for his friend stirred Achilles to action, and now no enemy could withstand his wrath. Thetis brought him new armour from the forge of Hephaestus, and Achilles tracked Hector through the Trojan ranks with murder in his heart. The river-god of the Scamander raised a barrier of water against Achilles, but Hephaestus dried up the river with a flaming torch and Achilles sent the Trojans reeling in panic into the city. Some desperate act was needed, so Hector, despite the pleas of Priam, went out to meet Achilles hand to hand. But when he saw the grim army of the Achaeans, and the raging hero in the lead, his courage failed him. He turned to run, but Achilles pursued him three times around the walls, caught him and transfixed him through the body. The hushed citizens watched in horror from the walls as the silence of death settled on Hector. In triumph, Achilles hitched the corpse to his chariot and dragged it through the dust to his camp.

Both armies paused, as if stunned, then resumed the war with a more hectic fury, striving, as if at the last gasp, for a victory that eluded them as food and drink eluded Tantalus in the Underworld. Penthesileia brought her Amazon women to the aid of Priam. Achilles was half in love with the beautiful queen, but he killed her. And when deformed Thersites, the foul-mouthed demagogue, mocked him for his lust and cruelty, Achilles shut the man's mouth forever with a blow of the fist. Then Priam's half-brother Memnon brought his Ethiopians from the deserts of the south and did such damage that Achilles begged Zeus to judge between himself and Memnon. Memnon's fate sank on the scales of Zeus, so Achilles confronted the Ethiopian and slew him. His dark followers turned into birds which circled faithfully around his tomb.

But now Achilles' glory had run its course. His violent pride offended the gods, and he owed Apollo a death for killing Tenes. In a skirmish by the Scaean Gate, Apollo guided the hand of Paris, drew the bow and sent a fatal arrow to Achilles' heel, his only vulnerable part. After a solemn and magnificent funeral, Odysseus and the greater Ajax competed for the dead man's arms. Agamemnon, who valued Odysseus' intelligence above the brute strength of Ajax, gave Odysseus the award and Ajax, in injured pride, swore a swift revenge. But Athene distracted him with madness, and instead of attacking those who had insulted him, he killed a flock of sheep. When he saw what he had done, he committed suicide in shame.

Now, when Zeus had assessed what the Fates had allotted to each man, he prepared a close to the great circle of this war. The prophets on both sides, speaking from the gods, made it known that Troy would not fall without Heracles' bow and arrows and without the presence of Achilles' son. Moreover, so long as Athene's Palladium rested in the citadel, the city was safe. First, Philoctetes was rescued from his long, painful exile on Lemnos, and, when he was cured of his festering wound, he put Heracles' bow to good use, killing Paris with a poisoned arrow. Then Neoptolemus, Achilles' son, was summoned from Scyros. Though Neoptolemus was only an untried youth, Odysseus dressed him in his father's armour, and the Achaeans took heart from his presence. But the Palladium, guarded within Athene's shrine, seemed beyond reach. Once again, Odysseus set his daring and fertile mind to the problem. He had himself whipped and disguised as the most miserable of beggars. Then, with the help of Diomedes, he wormed his way through the defences of Troy, killed the sleeping guards and, carrying the Palladium, crawled back to safety down a muddy drain.

Troy was now ready to topple, but it needed the final push, and Athene inspired a stratagem to achieve this. The craftsmen Epeius built a gigantic wooden horse with a hollow interior in which were hidden fifty chosen warriors. Then Agamemnon and the fleet sailed away, but only as far as Tenedos, leaving behind a certain Sinon, who let himself be taken prisoner. Railing against those treacherous colleagues who had left him behind, and cold-blooded Odysseus in particular, Sinon offered to help the Trojans. When they wondered at the wooden horse, he showed them the inscription: 'A thank-offering to Athene for our safe return home.' The horse was too big for the city gates, but Sinon insinuated that if it could be moved within the walls to Athene's temple, the city would be impregnable. Cassandra cried out in protest, fearing the gifts of the enemy, and the prophet Laocoön added his voice to her warning. But when two serpents came from the sea to strangle Laocoön and his sons, the Trojans' doubts were silenced. They breached the walls, put the horse on rollers and dragged it into the city.

While the Trojans celebrated and feasted, the men in the horse waited for night. Some Trojans, still suspicious, poked the wooden belly with spears, and Helen walked around the horse calling to heroes she had known in the voices of their wives. Some would have replied, but Odysseus clapped a hand over their mouths. In the night, when the Trojan guards were drunk with joy and wine, Sinon lit a beacon to call back the fleet, and the warriors quietly slid down a rope into the careless city.

In eerie moonlight, the massacre began. Fleeing Trojans, men, women and children, were put to the sword. Old King Priam, hardly able to hold a spear, was cut down in his own courtyard by Neoptolemus. Diophobus, the new guardian of Helen, was butchered by Menelaus who then turned on his guilty wife. But her beauty disarmed him, as it did all men, and he allowed her to live. Noble Trojan women were gathered as prizes and taken into slavery. Agamemnon took Cassandra,

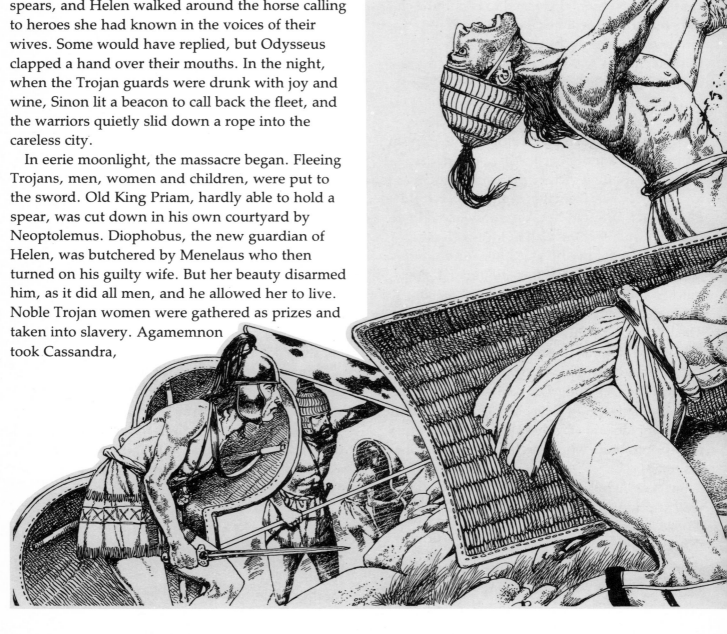

and Neoptolemus claimed Hector's widow Andromache. Even the dead received their share of the spoils. Polyxena, Priam's youngest daughter, was sacrificed at the tomb of Achilles, to appease the ghost of the bloodthirsty hero. Queen Hecabe witnessed it all: her sons killed one by one, her daughter violated and enslaved, her husband felled at her feet like an ox at the altar. Odysseus took her as his prize, but the gods transformed the tragic queen into a surly dog, howling despair to an indifferent world.

In the dawn, streets slippery with blood were empty and silent. Having set Troy ablaze, the Achaeans left the dead city.

## Homer and history

Scholars disagree sharply about how much history is to be found in Homer's two great epics, the *Iliad* and the *Odyssey*.

To believe that they contain reliable historical evidence, we must assume that they originally described accurately contemporary events and conditions; and that this description survived intact through all the combinations and recombinations, elaborations and additions made from one generation of minstrels to the next. It does, however, seem more likely that what would survive in such a process would be haphazard details of such things as weapons, furniture, social customs, places. The narratives in which these details were embedded would reflect much later stages of the four-hundred-year transition from the Mycenaean world to that of Ionia in the eighth century B C.

If Homer's description of the minstrel who sings to the courtiers of King Alcinous of Phaeacia, reflects the professional style of the minstrels who created materials for the Homeric epics, then it seems clear that they sang to entertain their audiences, not to instruct them in the facts about their past.

Nevertheless there are a few scholars who believe that the *Iliad* and the *Odyssey* are more or less reliable guides to late Bronze Age history, just as there are a few who go to the opposite extreme, believing that there never was a Trojan War and that the *Iliad* is essentially poetic fantasy.

Most scholars are more cautious. A great deal is known about the late Bronze Age that was unknown 150 years ago. The discovery of the remains of Troy, Mycenae and Cnossus were all surprises, so was the discovery that the inscriptions on clay tablets found at Cnossus and in the Mycenaean palaces on the Greek mainland were in Greek and could be deciphered.

There may be more surprises in the next 150 years.

The safest assumption seems to be that the realities of life during several different stages of Greek history have become inextricably mixed up in the epics. For instance, no one has been able to make sense of a Homeric battle. The incidents are vivid, the deaths often gruesomely realistic and the leading warriors characterized with great skill, but the tactics of individuals and the strategy of the commanders are incomprehensible.

This is partly because three different styles of warfare, and the weapons and armour appropriate to them, have been intermingled. At one moment the combatants seem about to engage in Bronze Age chariot warfare, but the actual fighting they do is single combat, chieftain against chieftain, each attacking his opponent with one javelin or two javelins or a thrusting spear or quite often with a stone picked up for the purpose. This seems more like early Iron Age than Bronze Age warfare. Then there are the massed ranks of the common soldiers who are drawn up before the fighting begins, as if for an infantry battle (a seventh century B C development) but never seem to do anything worth mentioning when the action is in progress.

If Homer's battles reflect several layers of Greek military history, so several layers of social and political history are probably reflected in the life styles of his heroes. Attempts to construct a portrait of Mycenaean society from the adventures of Odysseus and Telemachus are not convincing. The real Mycenaean palaces were equipped with busy scribes keeping meticulous accounts of the palace's business activities; they can hardly have resembled the homely palaces of Homer's kings.

If there really was a Trojan War, then the war and the warriors, their homes and their way of life must have been very unlike what is described by Homer.

# THE WANDERINGS OF ODYSSEUS

## The journey

From his earliest days Odysseus was renowned for cunning, luck and quick thinking. After all, was he not the grandson of Autolycus, the notorious thief and trickster? If one man were fated to survive the Trojan war, the chances were it would be Odysseus. He, among all others, would make a safe return. He would survive, but at the cost of pain and infinite weariness. So the oracle had warned him, even before he left Penelope and little Telemachus for Troy. Poseidon, the Earth-Shaker, became his enemy. Sea and sky and winds would conspire against him with all the bitterness a god could muster, before his foot rested once more on the familar beach of Ithaca.

After the victory at Troy, Odysseus embarked the men of his homeland in twelve ships and put the burning towers of the fallen city behind him. The first landfall of the little fleet was at Ismarus, in Thrace, where the men of Ithaca, unable to put their warlike habit aside, made a piratical raid on the Cicones. They sacked the city, sparing only a priest of Apollo, who gave them skins of strong wine in gratitude. But while Odysseus and his men were carousing, the Cicones rallied and drove them back to the ships with heavy losses. Struck by a violent north-east gale, the fleet was blown through the many islands of the Cyclades to Cape Malea, at the southern point of the Peloponnese. Now Odysseus had only to double the cape and sail the short distance up the Ionian sea to his island home. So near, and yet it was out of reach.

The foul weather continued. The ships were driven south to the land of the Lotus-Eaters. Odysseus sent men to explore but, having tasted the fruit of the lotus, they at once forgot their homes, longing only to settle into the forgetful indolence of the land. Odysseus found them with vague, smiling eyes and forced them at sword point back to the ships. Then he fled from their enchantments.

They sailed on until a need for supplies made Odysseus beach his fleet on a small green island inhabited only by goats. Searching the opposite coast with his own crew, he took a goatskin of wine and went to investigate an inviting cave. Inside were goats, milk and cheese, so Odysseus and his men feasted and made themselves at home. Towards evening, with a shaking of the ground, a giant with a single round eye in the middle of his forehead drove a flock of sheep into the cave and closed the opening with a weighty boulder. For this was the home of the Cyclops Polyphemus. This son of Poseidon lived in that remote land with his fellow Cyclopes, once the scourge of the gods but now dwelling peacefully in rural isolation.

When the giant noticed his visitors, Odysseus, in the name of Zeus, asked for hospitality. But having only contempt for the gods, Polyphemus laughed. He grabbed two of the crew, dashed out their brains and ate them. Next morning, after breakfasting on two more, he took his sheep to pasture but carefully shut in his prisoners with the huge rock. Now Odysseus pondered what to do. He might kill the giant, but he and his men together could never move the massive door-stone. After long thought, he saw another way. He sharpened a heavy log of olive-wood, which he then tempered in the fire. That evening, when the Cyclops had eaten two more men and was feeling full and relaxed, Odysseus offered him strong wine from his goatskin. Unused to wine, Polyphemus was soon happily befuddled and asked the name of his benefactor.

'My name is Nobody,' replied cunning Odysseus.

'Well, Nobody,' Polyphemus promised, 'in return for your gift of wine, I'll eat you last.'

But in the night, when the giant had collapsed into drunken snores, Odysseus and his men re-heated the stake and drove it into the Cyclops' single eye. The blinded Polyphemus woke up roaring for help. But when his fellow giants came running, Polyphemus could only shout, 'Nobody has blinded me', so the other Cyclopes thought he had a delirious fever and advised him to pray to his father Poseidon for relief. In the morning, with his flock clamouring to be let out, Polyphemus opened the cave and placed himself in the entrance to check each animal. But Odysseus had yoked the sheep into groups of three, tying one of his men under each group, while he himself clung to the thick wool beneath the largest ram. As the flock left the cave, Polyphemus stroked the back of each animal but found no one. And when he came to the great ram he paused and wondered, for the ram was usually the first to burst from the cave. He caressed his favourite ram with affectionate words, then he let it go.

Joyfully, Odysseus and his men ran to the ship, driving the Cyclops' flock before them. When they were on board, and pulling to safety, Odysseus could not contain his triumph. 'Cyclops!' he shouted at the wounded giant. 'It was not Nobody who blinded you. It was Odysseus of Ithaca.' In rage and despair Polyphemus prayed to his father Poseidon for vengeance and hurled pieces of the mountain towards the hateful voice which taunted him. Though the ship was nearly swamped, the waves from the huge rocks carried Odysseus out of range. But Poseidon, the Earth-Shaker, listened to the prayer of his son Polyphemus.

Rejoining the rest of his fleet, Odysseus sailed to the island of Aeolus, who was the guardian of the winds. The sailors were well-received, and entertained for a month. And when the time came to depart, Aeolus presented Odysseus with a bag in which all the winds were secured, except the West Wind which would fan the fleet gently towards Ithaca. Odysseus navigated until the smoke of his homeland was within sight. Then he

slept, exhausted. As he slept, his men, suspecting that the bag of the winds contained treasure, opened it. Out rushed the rough angry airs and carried the ships helplessly back to their starting point. Aeolus was not pleased to have his guests return and his gift wasted. He would have nothing further to do with men who were so foolish and so detested by the gods.

Deprived of wind, the chastened fleet rowed away and journeyed for several days to a new land of deep inlets and high, gloomy rocks. Cautiously, Odysseus anchored in open water, though the rest of the fleet entered a narrow harbour and three men set out to explore. They met a girl drawing water who pointed the way to the palace. As they made their way towards it, the people of that land, the giant Laestrygones, sprang on them and chased them back to the harbour where they threw rocks on to the penned-in ships. The ships were sunk and all the sailors either drowned or harpooned. Seeing the carnage from the open water, Odysseus cut his anchor rope and his crew rowed for their lives.

Reduced to a single ship, and hardly knowing which way to go, Odysseus steered to the east with the prevailing wind and after a long time came to Aeaea. This was the island of Circe, the sorceress and mistress of all enchantments. Reluctantly drawing lots to spy out the land, a party led by Eurylochus made their way through pleasant country to a palace in a clearing around which lions and wolves were prowling. These wild animals, usually so fierce, seemed to want to lick the hands of the sailors. Within the palace, they heard a woman singing and the click of a shuttle going to and fro in a loom. They called out a greeting and Circe came smiling to the door, inviting them to enter and eat.

Though Eurylochus was suspicious, his companions went in happily and sat down to eat, while Eurylochus peeped through a window. Circe set down many good things, but the food and drink were mixed with magic drugs. When the meal was finished, the sorceress tapped each sailor with a wand, changing men into swine. Then she drove them out to join the cattle and the wild beasts in the field, all of whom had once been men. In haste, Eurylochus brought the news to Odysseus, who took his sword and set off to the rescue. On the way, the god Hermes, in the form of a youth, fell in with Odysseus, warning him against the tricks of Circe and giving him, as an antidote to her magic, the divine herb call moly, a plant with black roots and milky flowers known only to the gods.

At the palace, Odysseus accepted the invitation to eat. But when Circe touched him with her wand, the moly protected him. He drew his sword and forced her to her knees. 'Spare me,' she begged, 'and you will reign with me, sharing my bed of love.' But Odysseus would not give way until she had promised to restore his men and sworn never to harm him with her spells. After a night of love, Circe went to the pig-sty and rubbed the animals with an ointment that made them not only human again, but younger and more handsome than before. Then Odysseus consented to live with Circe, and he and his crew stayed on Aeaea for a year in the greatest ease and contentment.

But at last homesickness tugged at Odysseus' heart, and he asked Circe to help him home. She agreed to let him go, but told him that for directions he must call up the dead from the House of Hades and seek his fate from the shade of the blind soothsayer Teiresias. The North Wind would blow his ship to the grove of willow and black poplar, by the stream of Oceanus, where the road descended to the darkness of Tartarus. Next morning, Odysseus cast off but did not notice that Elpenor, the youngest of the crew, was missing. The fellow had climbed on the palace roof, to cool his head after too much wine, and had fallen to his death in the night.

At Persephone's grove, by the mouth of Hades, Odysseus did as Circe had told him. He slaughtered a ram and a black ewe and let their blood flow into a trench. The shades of the dead came clamouring to drink, but Odysseus held them off with his sword, waiting for Teiresias. Elpenor came out of the dark, complaining that his body lay unburied on Aeaea. Odysseus promised to return

and give him an honourable burial. Then Anticleia, Odysseus' own mother, appeared and even she was not allowed to drink. At last, Teiresias came to the trench, and when he had greedily lapped the blood he gave Odysseus his advice.

Poseidon, said the soothsayer, was angry with Odysseus, because he had blinded Polyphemus. But if Odysseus kept his crew in order, so that his men did no harm to the sacred cattle of Helius, his ship would arrive home safely; if not, then Odysseus alone would reach home, to find his house in turmoil, his property wasted, and his wife in danger. But he would have his revenge. Then he would satisfy Poseidon with a great sacrifice and live out a prosperous old age until death came to him from the sea.

Odysseus thanked Teiresias and then allowed his mother Anticleia to drink from the trench. She gave him news from Ithaca, of Penelope and Telemachus and his father Laertes. After Anticleia had said farewell, a host of other shades came to drink. He met, with sad recollection, his old comrades-in-arms Achilles and Agamemnon and Ajax, and others who had fallen at Troy. He saw Minos on his judgement seat, and witnessed the tortures of the great sinners, such as Tantalus and Sisyphus, and spoke with the ghost of mighty Heracles. But now the shades of the dead, thirsty for blood, crowded so thickly around the trench that Odysseus was afraid of the grim congregation and retreated quickly into the land of light and living.

Having arrived at Aeaea once more, Odysseus gave Elpenor a decent burial, with an oar planted on the mound as a memorial. Then Circe welcomed Odysseus back from the House of Hades and, taking him by the hand, warned him of the perils of his journey. First, he must pass by the island of the Sirens, where those creatures with the faces of women and the bodies of birds, sat among the heaped bones of their victims, and cast the spell of their songs over all travellers. Then, avoiding the Clashing Rocks which nearly brought Jason's *Argo* to disaster, he would come to the greater danger of Scylla and Charybdis. If he survived these, then the island of Thrinacie awaited him, where the sacred herds of the sun god Helius roamed free. These animals must not be harmed, as Teiresias had already warned. If Odysseus passed safely by Thrinacie, the way home was clear and certain; if not, his path was dark and uncertain and sown with many dangers.

In the dawn, Circe sent the ship a good wind which blew swiftly towards the Sirens. When the island came in sight, the wind dropped as if lulled by some evil hand, and Odysseus made his preparations, as Circe had instructed him. He plugged the ears of his crew with wax and ordered them to row briskly along the shore. But as he was determined to hear the song of the Sirens, he had himself bound to the mast and made his men swear that, come what may, they would not untie him. Then, as the ship slipped by, the song of the Sirens ravished his ears, and they beckoned to him, telling of past suffering on the plain of Troy. With angry gestures, Odysseus demanded to be released, but Eurylochus only tightened the bonds.

In this way the Sirens were left safely astern. But hardly was the wax taken from the sailors' ears when they were terrified by the spume of white spray and the roar of water that issued from the strait of Scylla and Charybdis. On one side of the narrows was a cave in a vast, smooth cliff where Scylla lived. This monster had six fierce yapping heads on the ends of snaking necks which roved and weaved over the sea, snapping up mariners from every passing ship. On the other side, below a massive fig tree, the whirlpool of Charybdis sucked down the sea and spewed it up three times a day.

Odysseus had been advised by Circe to steer by the side of Scylla, for not even Poseidon could withstand the force of Charybdis. And it was better to lose six men than the entire ship. Pale with fear the rowers bent to the oars, skimming the ship under the cliff of Scylla, while Odysseus stood armed on the foredeck. But he could do nothing. The six heads of Scylla plucked out six sailors, who disappeared into the white mist screaming 'Odysseus!' But the ship sped on into clear waters

and the cries died helplessly in the air.

Overcome by grief and exhaustion, the crew wanted to land and rest when the island of Thrinacie approached. Odysseus remembered the warning and urged them to continue without pause, but the angry voices of the crew overruled him. Reluctantly, he anchored but made each man swear that on no account would even the smallest of the sacred cattle be harmed. Then they landed at a pleasant cove, with the sacred herds of the Sun grazing placidly nearby. At first there was no temptation to harm them. But for a month contrary winds held them ashore and, as their stores ran out, the men began to mutter. One morning, as Odysseus slept, they made a decision. They killed the choicest cattle, but dedicated some to Helius in humble sacrifice. If the god was not satisfied with that, then let him sink the ship, for it was better to take their chance than to die by starvation.

When Odysseus awoke he was horrified. Quickly launching the ship, he tried to leave the island far behind. But Helius cried out to Zeus against the insolence of men, and the Thunderer sent storms and thunderbolts to strike the ship. The mast crashed down, killing the helmsman. The ship foundered and all were drowned, except Odysseus who clung to some wreckage as a makeshift raft. The storm drove him back to Charybdis, where he took a desperate hold on the spreading branch of the great fig tree just as the whirling waters were sucked down. He was left hanging in the air but managed to hold on until Charybdis threw up his battered raft again. In slack water he dropped into the sea, mounted his raft and paddled to safety. After nine days he drifted ashore on the island of Ogygia where Calypso, the fair daughter of Thetis, had a kind welcome for his bruised body and dejected spirit.

In the secluded cavern, overhung with vines and fruits, the nymph Calypso tended Odysseus with every comfort, and he shared her soft bed. But though she offered him immortality and eternal youth if he would stay with her, his heart still yearned towards Ithaca. For seven years he lived with Calypso, lapped in luxury but without peace

of mind. Then Athene, seeing her favourite day by day staring forlornly out to sea, interceded with Zeus on his behalf. And since Poseidon was away from Olympus, Zeus sent Hermes to Ogygia with orders to release Odysseus. Sadly, Calypso obeyed the will of Zeus. She gave Odysseus tools and suitable materials and with her advice he made a sturdy boat, which she provisioned with good supplies of food and drink. Then the nymph bathed him, dressed him in splendid robes, and bade him farewell.

With the stars of the Great Bear on his left hand, as Calypso had told him, Odysseus sailed for seventeen days, almost to the land of the Phaeacians. Then Poseidon, returning from a visit to Ethiopia, noticed the boat upon the sea and, angry that Zeus had helped Odysseus behind his back, swore that the wanderer would have a bellyful of trouble yet. Massing the clouds and stirring the sea with his trident, Poseidon swept Odysseus overboard with a huge wave. Hampered by his heavy robes, Odysseus clung to the planks of the boat and lamented his misfortune. But the sea-goddess Ino-Leucothea took pity on him. Alighting in the form of a sea-mew, with a magic veil in her mouth, she told Odysseus to cast off his cumbersome clothes and plunge into the stormy sea with the veil around his waist. It would carry him safely to shore.

After Poseidon had returned grumbling to his underwater palace, Athene smoothed the sea and Odysseus swam on. Two days later, utterly exhausted and battered by the inhospitable rocks of the coast, Odysseus reached a river mouth on the island of the Phaeacians. He kissed the ground in thanks and collapsed under the shelter of some bushes.

While he slept, Athene visited Nausicaa, King Alcinous' lovely daughter in a dream, persuading her to take her clothes and wash them in the stream. When the work was done, Nausicaa and her women began to play with a ball, tossing it amongst them, until one missed her catch and the ball splashed in the stream. The girl gave a shriek and Odysseus, awakened suddenly, crawled out from his cover, hiding his nakedness behind a bushy branch.

The serving-girls fled in dismay, but Nausicaa stood her ground and Odysseus, despite his wild looks, won her sympathy with the power of his words. Nausicaa hurried to the palace to prepare the way for this unlucky stranger, then, under a pall of healing mist provided by Athene's art, Odysseus entered the city where King Alcinous lived in splendour.

King Alcinous listened as the stranger made his request: a ship and sailors to carry him safely home to his own land. Then, when drink-offerings had been made to Zeus, the king ordered a ship to be made ready. And that night Odysseus slept at peace.

But Alcinous could not let his guest go without an honourable departure. After games and feasting, the bard Demodocus took his lyre and began to tell the great deeds of gods and men. He sang of the war at Troy and the famous fights before the walls. He celebrated Achilles' valour and Odysseus' cunning and the skill of Epeius who made the wooden horse. Then Odysseus could bear the song no more, and with tears in his eyes he stopped the bard. Gently, Alcinous asked him the cause of his dismay. Odysseus answered: 'I am Odysseus, Laertes' son. All the world knows my subtlety, and my fame has reached heaven. But my home and heart lie under the clear skies of Ithaca.' Then, to the amazement of the court, he told the whole story of his trials and travels.

Next day, laden with costly gifts, Odysseus embarked on a ship manned by Phaeacian sailors, which carried him swiftly to Ithaca. As Odysseus, worn out by troubles, was asleep when the ship anchored in the bay of Phorcys, the sailors put him undisturbed on the sand with his gifts around him. Then they went quietly home. But Poseidon was still angry. Since Odysseus' homecoming was the will of Zeus, the Earth-Shaker could only take out his fury on the Phaeacians. As their ship returned to harbour, he struck it with the flat of his hand and turned it to stone, as a warning to others that it was dangerous to give safe-conduct on the seas without the permission of Poseidon.

# The homecoming

When Odysseus awoke, on a strange beach, he did not recognize his homeland. As he began hiding his gifts, Athene came by disguised as a shepherd and started to question him. Cautious as ever, Odysseus invented a devious tale, but Athene made herself known with a smile: 'What a rogue you are, dear Odysseus. A god could hardly match your tricks.' She told him where he was and how matters stood in his palace. An insolent crowd of one hundred and twelve suitors, from Ithaca and nearby islands, were besieging Penelope for marriage, wasting her property and eating all her stocks of food. Moreover, they were plotting to kill her son Telemachus when he returned from searching for his father. Having warned him of the dangerous times in Ithaca, Athene disguised Odysseus as an old beggar and led him to the hut of Eumaeus, the faithful palace swineherd.

Then Athene flew to Sparta to bring Telemachus safely home, taking him also, when he landed, to Eumaeus' hut. In a private moment Odysseus revealed himself to his son, and they wept together after the long separation. Then they plotted the downfall of the suitors. Telemachus returned to the palace and Odysseus followed after, to spy out the land. As he went, looking so old in beggarly rags, the goat-herd Melantheus gave him a contemptuous kick but at the palace gate, the old hunting dog Argus, lying mangy and dying on the dung-heap, recognized his long-lost master and tried to wag his pathetic tail.

Within the hall of the palace Odysseus saw the suitors, lolling on idle couches, with little to do but quarrel and feast. To test them, Odysseus begged for alms, though he got nothing but blows and bruises, especially from their leader Antinous, who hit him with a foot-stool. And when Irus, a local beggar, resented the competition from Odysseus, the amused suitors pressed them to fight, offering a pudding of blood and offal to the winner. Odysseus hitched up his rags, showing unsuspected muscles, and felled Irus with one blow. Penelope, hearing of these antics in her gracious palace, was ashamed and sent a woman to invite this sturdy beggar to talk with her. He had travelled far and might have news of her husband.

In the darkened hall, with the suitors gone to their slothful beds, Odysseus told Telemachus to remove all weapons and armour from the walls. Then he was ready to see Penelope. Safe in his disguise, Odysseus spun his wife a fanciful story, but gave her strong hope for the imminent return of her husband. Then he heard from her lips the history of her persecution by the suitors.

First, she had put them off, saying that the oracle promised her husband's return. But as the years passed, they became more insolent and importunate. Then she said she could give no decision until the shroud for her father-in-law Laertes was woven. For three years she worked at her loom during the day and every night unpicked the cloth. Now her little trick had been detected and she could delay her decision no longer.

They finished talking and Penelope, weeping for her own distress and for the hard life of the beggar, ordered the aged nurse Eurycleia to bathe the feet and weary legs of the sympathetic stranger. As Eurycleia began her task she saw a scar on the beggar's thigh which, she recognized, was the result of a boar-hunt wound to Odysseus many years ago. But before she could cry out her happy news, Odysseus gripped her throat and swore her to silence.

Next day was the feast of Apollo and all the household worked hard and long to make a banquet for the suitors. Amid their taunts, Odysseus took a shabby old stool to a strategic place in the doorway. Then Agelaus gave Penelope an ultimatum from his friends and rivals: their patience was stretched to the limit, and Penelope must now choose one of them. When Telemachus seemed reluctantly to agree, Penelope fetched Odysseus' great bow, long unused, from the store-house. In silence she advanced into the hall and then announced that she would marry the man who could string the bow and shoot an arrow through the rings of twelve axes set in a row, as Odysseus himself used to do.

One by one, the suitors failed to bend the stiff bow. While they were struggling with this, Odysseus slipped out, declared himself to his loyal servants Eumaeus and the herdsman Philoetius, and ordered them to clear the palace and secure the doors. Then Odysseus returned to the feast and humbly asked permission to try his strength against the mighty bow. Amid jeers and insults, Telemachus allowed his father to take the bow. As easily as a musician setting a new string, Odysseus bent the bow and strung it. And taking an arrow from the full quiver, he sent it whizzing straight through the rings of all twelve axes. Then, with sword and spear in hand, Telemachus ran to his father in the doorway. Together, they stood at the entrance to the long hall, looking calmly over the sea of astonished suitors.

'The die is cast,' cried Odysseus, throwing off his rags. 'Now for another target!' And his arrow pierced the neck of Antinous. Then the fight was on. The suitors rushed to the walls for arms and armour but, finding them gone, drew their short swords and swarmed towards the two figures in the doorway. Steadily, Odysseus sent arrow after arrow to their deadly marks, while Telemachus lunged and thrust with his long spear. When the arrows ran out, and things began to look black for father and son, Athene stiffened their resolve, fluttering over the battle in the form of a swallow.

At last, the fight was won. On the suitors' side, only the bard and herald were spared, for their persons were sacrosanct. The guilty men and women of the household were rooted out. The maids who had slept with the idle drones were hanged in a row, and the goat-herd Melantheus, the suitors' servile friend, had his hands and feet cut off and thrown to the dogs.

For a time after the battle, Odysseus and Penelope sat wearily apart in the empty hall, hardly daring to trust each other, for the world and the past seemed too strange to fathom. Then the resentment, pain and suffering of twenty years washed away, and they came with tears of joy into each others' arms.

United at last with Penelope, and with his father Laertes, Odysseus was not quite at the end of the trail of troubles which the Fates had spun for him. The clans of the suitors took up the blood-feud against the house of Odysseus. But after a skirmish, in which even aged Laertes showed the power of his arm, the voice of Athene ordered an end to all hostilities. And then great Zeus gave to her command the irrevocable stamp of his authority, striking the ground with a thunderbolt, so that men once consumed by hatred now had only awe in their hearts. They laid down their arms and swore peace in the name of the gods.

Only Poseidon remained unappeased. So Odysseus, as Teiresias had instructed him, made one more pilgrimage. Carrying an oar on his shoulder, he travelled to the land of Thesprotis, going farther and farther from the sea until he reached a people who used no salt and who knew nothing of ships or the wide water. Then Odysseus planted the oar in the ground and sacrificed a ram, a bull and a boar to Poseidon. The Earth-Shaker was satisfied, and the unequal enmity between god and human was laid to rest.

No one is certain about the last days of Odysseus. Some say he lived to a ripe old age and then death came to him, as had been foretold, from the sea. Others say that Telegonus, his own son by the sorceress Circe, slew him. In a small fray on an unimportant island, Telegonus thrust at an unrecognized stranger with a lance tipped by a sting-ray's spine, and killed his father by mistake.

But all this, for the true relation is known only to the gods, is merely a part of the complex pattern of the song of mankind. For the gods weave misfortunes into the lives of men so that generations to come may sing these stories.

## Who was Homer?

Who was Homer? When and where did he live and compose the two epics? Was he one man, or two, or several? The *Iliad* and the *Odyssey* and several other poems were from the earliest times believed to have been written by a man named Homer. Much later (from the third century AD onwards) scholars raised questions about their authorship. These questions were raised again by a French scholar at the end of the seventeenth century, by a German scholar at the end of the eighteenth century and have been debated ever since.

The problem of Homer's identity arises because in the early centuries of Greek civilization there were no accurate accounts of the lives of the poets—or if there were, they did not survive. So all that can be known is what the poets reveal about themselves in their poetry. Hesiod chose to reveal quite a lot about himself, Homer nothing at all. Scraps of traditional information were put together to make up biographies of a sort. Homer was said to have been born in Ionia, in the city of Smyrna; or Colophon; or on the island of Chios, or on Cyprus. His father was called Maeon, or Mnesagoras, or Daemon; or he was the son of Telemachus and grandson of Odysseus. Homer's real name, it was said, was Meles, or Melesigenes, or Altes. He was renamed Homer because he became blind and that was what the blind were called in his city; or else it was because his father had been sent to the Persians as a hostage (*Homeros* means 'hostage' in Greek). Most of this was very properly disregarded by the scholars in Alexandria who were the first to study the epics critically. They were concerned mainly to explain obscure words and passages and to identify from the many texts which were then in existence what had been Homer's original composition. This meant comparing different versions of the text, correcting errors made by slaves when copying from one papyrus roll to another and marking lines or episodes that they considered not to have been part of the original poems.

*Continued over page*

In the course of their studies they became puzzled that one man could have written two epics which were so different in tone and subject matter and which contradicted each other in certain details.

Some explained this by supposing that Homer had composed the *Iliad* when in the prime of life and the *Odyssey* in his old age. Others decided that there must have been two Homers, the author of the *Odyssey* being a younger man who had been deeply influenced by the style of the *Iliad*.

The question of Homer's identity was revived in 1795 when the German scholar F.A. Wolf asserted that since no one practised writing in Homer's lifetime no single poet could at that time have created and passed down to later generations an epic as lengthy as the *Iliad*, which consists of over 15,000 lines of verse. He claimed that both epics arose from a long tradition of minstrelsy—poems improvised by different minstrels as they sang of great deeds performed in battles of the past and of the heroes who performed them. By this tradition a large number of short episodes or lays was passed on to professional reciters. Homer did not actually compose the different verses but was a literary genius who collected them together and wove them into two epic masterpieces.

Then, in the 1920s, two American scholars shed new light on the way in which Homer's epics could have been preserved before being written down. They were studying improvised poetry, sung to a musical instrument, which was at that time still a live art in Yugoslavia

The Yugoslav poets whose songs they recorded sang of the exploits of legendary heroes in the disastrous struggles of the Serbs against the Turks more than five hundred years earlier. Their songs were very long and they sang without any script (they were illiterate) and on themes chosen from a limited repertoire by their audiences. Although they improvised each verse, they did so within a strict and traditional framework which enabled them to memorize the words and the sequence of events; that is to say there were a limited number of phrases they could use to describe any particular event and the events themselves were limited in number and unfolded in a limited number of ways. The performances produced a style of poetry strikingly like that of the Homeric epics. Like the Yugoslav poems, the *Iliad* and the *Odyssey* include stock epithets. Achilles, for example, is always 'swift-footed' even when he is refusing to budge from his tent: Odysseus is 'full of wiles' or 'noble' or 'indomitable', the particular word being chosen to fit the rhythm of the line rather than the occasion being described. There are also stock phrase patterns. If a hero makes a speech it is introduced in a very limited number of phrases, such as 'in reply swift-footed Achilles addressed him'; or 'strong-footed, noble Achilles addressed him first'. A new day always begins with the appearance of 'rosy-fingered dawn' even for Odysseus and his comrades when they are shut up in the darkness of the Cyclops' cave.

If the theory is correct, the poet who recited the epics would have learned by ear, in a long apprenticeship, the rhythms of the verse (which he could certainly not describe in terms of feet or syllables). The poetic language, with its stock phrases and descriptions, would be learned almost subconsciously, as a child learns to speak its mother tongue. The chief part that memory played in his performance was his memory of the events of the traditional stories, the names of the heroes whose actions are celebrated in them and details that had been incorporated into the versions of previous poets.

This theory still raises many questions. For what occasion could such lengthy epics as the *Iliad* and the *Odyssey* have been improvised? How did they come in the end to be written down? We know that they were recited after the time of Homer by professional reciters known as rhapsodes on the occasion of certain religious festivals. The structure and design of the epics seems to imply that somewhere in the course of transmission there was a stage that involved much planning and experiment. When precisely this happened and who was responsible remains a mystery. If you ask a modern scholar he or she will probably say that on historical and linguistic grounds the two great epics appear to have been composed about 750 BC. Versions of both in writing (not necessarily single copies of the entire text) must have existed by the seventh century BC. Beyond that everything is controversial.

# Books for further reading

The commentaries in this book have briefly explained the background to the myths but there is still a great deal of ancient Greek civilization to explore. All the main texts mentioned in the book are available in translation. Here are some suggestions for additional background reading:

## DICTIONARIES OF GREEK (AND ROMAN) MYTHS
A good dictionary of classical myth should have comprehensive alphabetical entries, genealogical tables, a list of the ancient sources for each myth and an index. Well-chosen illustrations are helpful but not essential. An excellent example: *The Dictionary of Classical Mythology* by Pierre Grimal, translated from the French by A. R. Maxwell-Hyslop, Blackwell 1986.

## THE INTERPRETATION OF GREEK MYTHS
*The Nature of Greek Myths* by G. S. Kirk, Penguin Books 1974. A comprehensive review of theories of myth and their application to Greek myths. Scholarly and lucidly written.
*Gods and Heroes of the Greeks, The Library of Apollodorus* translated with Introduction and Notes by Michael Simpson, University of Massachusetts Press 1976. This compendium of Greek myths was compiled some time in the first century AD or BC. The translator's notes discuss literary versions of the myths (ancient and modern) and current attempts to interpret them.

## MYTHS AND RELIGION
*The Greeks and their Gods* by W. K. C. Guthrie, Methuen 1950. An interesting and readable interpretation of how the Greeks saw their gods and goddesses. It was written before anthropological scholarship began to make its impact on the study of Greek myth and religion but is a good basis for exploring the new ideas.
*Greek Religion and Society* edited by P. E. Easterling and J. V. Muir, Cambridge University Press 1985. Eight essays written for sixth formers, undergraduates and the general reader on aspects of Greek religious belief and practice. They present up-to-date scholarship in a very readable and stimulating form and contain valuable notes for further reading.

## GENERAL HISTORIES OF ANCIENT GREECE
*Greece and the Hellenistic World* edited by John Boardman, Jasper Griffin and Oswyn Murray, Oxford University Press 1988. There are many good general histories but this one has five particular merits:
1. The fifteen scholars who contributed to it, all write interestingly and lucidly.
2. It treats the political, military, social and cultural (art, literature and religion) aspects of Greek history as parts of an integral whole.
3. The excellent illustrations are well chosen for their relevance to the text.
4. It has "Notes for further reading' which are helpfully informative.
5. It is available at a reasonable price in paperback.

## GENERAL HISTORIES OF GREEK LITERATURE
*A Short History of Greek Literature* by Jacqueline de Romilly, translated by Lillian Doherty, University of Chicago Press 1985.
*A History of Greek Literature* by Albin Lesky, translated by James Willis and Cornelis de Heer, Methuen 1966.
Both books cover Greek literature from Homer to the Emperor Julian, AD 360. Romilly's book is descriptive with lively critical comment. It is available in paperback. Lesky covers the same ground as Romilly in 900 pages by contrast with Romilly's 300, writing with such detail and learning that it would be surprising if there were any information anyone might wish to know about Greek literature that has been omitted. Definitely for reference, although very readable if taken in smallish doses.

## THE HOMERIC QUESTION
*Homer and the oral tradition* by G. S. Kirk, Cambridge University Press 1976. Over the last forty years there have been many books and articles discussing how the decipherment of Linear B affects the study of Homer, and the whole question of how the *Iliad* and the *Odyssey* were composed before writing became a common skill. The nine essays by Kirk contained in this book discuss the historic and literary aspects with a cool and lucid analysis of opposing arguments.

## TROY
*In search of the Trojan War* by Michael Wood, BBC Books 1987. The book gives fair treatment to conflicting opinions, discusses Troy and Homer from every angle, has splendid photographs and good maps and plans as well as a helpful bibliography.

## GREEK TRAGEDY
*Greek Tragedy in Action* by Oliver Taplin, Methuen 1978. Taplin discusses nine plays, illuminating the nature of Greek tragedy and its impact. The book is very lively and readable, but it is essential to read (in translation) the actual plays he discusses.

## GREEK ART
*A Handbook of Greek Art* by Gisela Richter, Phaidon (sixth edition) 1969. Informative, comprehensive, well-produced and well-illustrated, and in paperback.

## THE PHYSICAL AND ECONOMIC BACKGROUND TO GREEK HISTORY
*The Greek Commonwealth* by Alfred Zimmern, Oxford University Press 1911. Though many years old, this book is still well worth reading. Written, in the author's words, as 'the result of an attempt to make clear to myself what fifth century Athens was really like', it discusses the social, economic and geographical aspects of Ancient Athens which all the traditional histories of Greece left out.
*Classical Landscape with Figures* by Robin Osborne, George Philip 1987. Osborne starts with much more archaeological information at his disposal than Zimmern had and ranges more widely in space and time. He shows convincingly that the influence of geography was all-pervasive in the Greek world, for the simple reason that the needs of the countryside dominated life in the cities, not the reverse as has been the case in most civilizations.

## WOMEN IN ANCIENT GREECE
This has been a subject for serious study only for the last twenty or thirty years but has become a subject of great interest and importance. Appropriately the best books are by women scholars. Of these one of the earliest, and a minor classic, is *Goddesses, Whores, Wives and Slaves* by Sarah Pomeroy, Schocken Books, New York 1975. Another useful book is *Women in the Ancient World* by Gillian Clark, Oxford University Press, 1989, a 46-page survey and bibliography.

## HISTORICAL AND RELIGIOUS SITES
*Ancient Greece from the Air* by Raymond V. Schoder S. J., Thames and Hudson 1974. Now available from Old Vicarage Publications, The Old Vicarage, Reades Lane, Dane in Shaw, Congleton, Cheshire CW12 3LL. Descriptions, maps and aerial colour photographs of 140 Ancient Greek sites, including battle sites, temple precincts, theatres and athletic stadia.

# Index

*Page numbers in bold refer to illustrations*